About the author

Stefan Gates is a food adventurer and award-winning writer and broadcaster. He wrote and presented the highly acclaimed 'Cooking in the Danger Zone' (BBC2), 'Feasts' (BBC4), 'Full On Food' (BBC2) and the children's series 'Gastronuts' (BBC1 and CBBC) and is a regular panellist and guest on numerous radio and TV shows. He's been nominated for three Guild of Food Writers awards, and *Gastronauts* won the Gourmand World Cookbook award for best food literature book. When he's not eating and travelling he spends his time exploring the history, science, drama, religion and symbolism of the food that we eat. He lives in London with his long-suffering wife and his two daughters, who have very odd taste in food indeed.

First published in 2010 by Cassell Illustrated
a part of Octopus Publishing Group
Endeavour House, 189 Shaftesbury Avenue
London WC2H 8JY
www.octopusbooks.co.uk

A Hachette UK Company
www.hachette.co.uk

British Library Cataloguing-in-Publication Data.
A catalogue record for this book is available from the British Library.

Publisher: Lorraine Dickey
Contributing Editor: Lewis Esson
Researcher: Fiona Wilcock
Art Director: Jonathan Christie
Production Manager: Katherine Hockley

ISBN 978 1 84091 561 7
Printed in UK

Stefan Gates

on

E
NUM
BERS

Is your food really going to kill you?
The truth about E numbers

CASSELL
ILLUSTRATED

Contents

The fascinating, outrageous bit

This book is, in many ways, a celebration of E numbers. I'm well aware that this is deeply unfashionable and goes against the grain of public opinion, and I predict a deluge of scorn and anger raining down on me from my peers and colleagues for writing it. So, although I'm sure it's utterly futile, I'd like to start by making one thing very clear:

I love food, but I hate bullshit.

By food, I mean everything that's life affirming and pleasurable to eat. I'm your archetypal irritating food-obsessive: a man who daydreams about fine hams, who'll bore you to death with tales of artisan cheesemakers and arcane recipes, given half a chance. I get visibly agitated when I taste something truly special and I'm inevitably happiest cooking foods from conscientious producers who respect their land, animals and traditions. Heck, I know it's not a reason *not* to hate me, but I've even got an award from the Slow Food movement.

By bullshit, I mean the clichés, mantras, cherry-picked research, unquestioned nutritional assumptions and half-truths spread without a second thought by food writers, TV chefs, reporters and media nutritionists. The most damaging of these are the widely held beliefs that all E numbers are bad for you, that preservatives are unnecessary and that it's a conspiracy of faceless food manufacturers, scientists and the government – rather than ourselves – who are to blame for bad nutrition and food poisoning. The food industry does indeed cause some crippling environmental, social and medical problems (more about these later), but blaming E numbers for them is a lazy shortcut that skips over real issues of personal accountability for health.

I first started to doubt the hysteria about Es after reading Jeffrey Steingarten's brilliant 1999 essay 'Why Doesn't Everyone in China Have a Headache?' Then, when I started to talk to doctors, gastroenterologists and oncologists I found that they were exasperated with the public's obsession with Es, seeing them as a huge distraction from the really pressing health and nutrition issues that are *our* responsibilities, but which we (and I include myself here) are extremely reluctant to tackle because it's infinitely easier to blame Es in general as a business/science/government conspiracy. We all know what those health issues are: unbalanced diets, eating disorders, food poisoning, physical inactivity, obesity, excessive alcohol consumption and smoking. But these all take energy, abstinence and willpower to solve.

Like many natural foods, several Es have been proven to cause problems to a small proportion of consumers (for example, some colours are linked with hyperactivity in children, nitrates have been linked to bowel cancer and the preservative essential to wine-making can exacerbate asthma), but often the benefits of additives far outweigh the risks.

The public perception is that the food industry pours harmful additives into our food for no good reason except their own profit, causing widespread allergies, intolerances and all manner of other health problems. However, there's a gaping maw of difference between the perception and the reality, as the European Commission found out when it asked the Scientific Committee for Food to check exactly this. There were, indeed, people intolerant to additives, but not very many: 0.01–0.23%[*].

Interestingly, 2% of adults were found to have intolerance of all foods (around 1–3% of us are intolerant of cows' milk). However, the amount of people who *think* that additives cause them adverse reactions is much, much higher: around 7%, according to a huge study[**] carried out amongst 30,000 people in the 1980s. When those 7% were tested, only 3 people had reproducible reactions to additives. This is a tricky area in which to perform clinical studies, and cherry-picking of research facts is always a concern, but really... 3 people.

[*] 'Scientific Committee for Food. Report on Adverse Reactions to Food and Food Ingredients'. 1996
[**] http://archive.food.gov.uk/maff/archive/food/fac/facnews/issue2/page6.htm

I'm not suggesting that those who think they are intolerant of additives are stupid or paranoid, but I do think that amateur nutritionists and the headline-hungry media have a lot to answer for, because they are the people who've made us scared of our food.

That said, there are some disgusting rip-off foods out there in the shops and many of them contain lots of E numbers, but although it's tempting to think the additives are the problem, that's not really the case. Nor, if we're being rigorous about this, are the fats, salt or sugar with which they are packed (we need all of these in our diet). It's the *balance* of these substances alongside the protein, fibre, vitamins, minerals and so on that makes a diet healthy or otherwise, and that balance is our responsibility. Put another way, there's little nutritionally wrong with a single McDonalds Big Mac, or a posh rib-eye steak with pommes dauphinoise, for that matter. But a diet made up of lots of Big Macs (or rib-eye steaks and pommes dauphinoise) and nothing else is highly likely to end up causing you problems. The trouble is that a balanced diet of healthy home-cooked food takes thought, time and money that many people either can't or won't spend. Perhaps better education about food, cooking and nutrition is the solution. Blaming Es certainly isn't.

The grand conspiracy theories about a government-science-business complex poisoning us with E numbers increases public paranoia and thereby lays the foundations for another industry to counter the conspiracy. That industry is the media-savvy, multi-billion-pound nutritionist and nutritional supplement industry, which sells sometimes bizarre and inappropriate nutritional advice based on flimsy evidence or hearsay (see pages 53–7), expensive solutions such as detox products (there's no such thing outside the clinical treatment for drug addiction or poisoning), that homeopathic remedies are more than just placebos (don't get me started!) and some clinically unproven and often unnecessary supplements such as fish oil pills for better scholastic performance by school children.

These fish oils are a particularly murky £110m industry, and the excitement for them mainly comes from a massive trial by a large supplements manufacturer called Equazen. Together with Durham Council, they carried out a huge, shouty yet oddly unclinical study on 5,000 students backed up by massive publicity from the *Daily Mail* (Ben Goldacre describes this in excellent detail in *Bad Science*). After the study took place, the rate of improvement in Durham students getting five GCSE grades A to C actually fell from 5.5% to 3.5%. Just to be clear, exam grades improved as they often do, but at a much lower rate than the previous year! Never mind though, because parents are desperate people, and many of them are willing to part with 80p a day for these pills just on the hope that something – anything – might help.

One of the underlying problems in all this is that it is a little too easy to be a nutritionist. I'll show you how easy: I am a nutritionist. There, two seconds ago I was merely a sceptical food writer, but just by calling myself a nutritionist, I am one. You don't need any qualifications to call yourself a nutritionist, but doesn't it sound authoritatively medical? I could charge you £60 for a consultation if you were willing to cough up. On the other hand, you do need qualifications legally to call yourself a clinical dietitian, some of whom can be very good indeed, so I'd go and see one of those if you're worried about nutrition. I am sure this is possibly true of many professions. After all I have no formal qualifications as a food writer, but then no one is going to ask me what NOT to eat.

There are, of course, some excellent nutritionists out there who restrict themselves to advice based on clinically proven facts, but who are you to know if you're handing over your £60 to one of them, or to one of those bonkers ones off of the telly who thinks flax seed cures cancer, who thinks selling horny goat weed is a decent way to earn their crust and who prefers anecdotal evidence to double-blind placebo-controlled clinical trials?

At this point, however, I ought to make a confession. I've presented a few jolly TV shows about food and I used to be as guilty as anyone of using empty phrases such as 'It's full of chemicals', 'It's full of E numbers', or 'This'll have the kids bouncing off the walls' as a generic put-down for processed foods. I've also used empty, misleading phrases such as 'good, honest food', knowing deep down that there's no such thing. For instance, I've known for years that milk is a delicate balance of hundreds of chemicals hanging in a complex emulsion, none of which has any moral compass. They just *are*.

The trouble is that when you're cooking on TV you're often filling space with words because you're concentrating on not chopping off your fingers, but you need to keep talking. We call it 'chop-and-chat', and sometimes you're reduced to phatic communication, using phrases the public have heard a thousand times before. In retrospect, it was patronizing and lazy, but there's a pressure to conform to the jolly template of food programming, and I regret that I helped to propagate ill-considered clichés and mantras.

While filming these shows, some fantastic chefs have told me that they hate getting science in their food, and that cooking is art. Many chefs are unaware, or simply unwilling to admit, that they are experts in the thermodynamics of ovens and pans, actively denaturing proteins every time they cook meat and fish, and carrying out complex controlled reactions on amino acids and carbohydrates every time they brown something in a pan. Look, I know we like our food to feel natural and wholesome but, at the same time, all cooking involves changing the chemical state of foods by applying heat, emulsifying, whipping, kneading, etc., to make them safe, edible, attractive and enjoyable. Whether you like it or not, when you cook your food you are *processing* it.

You can be a great cook *without* knowing that the purest *daube de beouf* also contains a bunch of chemicals, including glutamates, antioxidants and thickeners that have been through chemical processes including the Maillard process (browning meats) and protein denaturing (cooking meat and fish), but it seems odd to deny the truth about it. All matter is at some level a collection of chemical substances – just as a glass of water is a soup of H_2O molecules. There are an estimated 500,000 naturally occurring chemicals in our diet. What surprised me most when I began to research Es is that many of them are naturally occurring, that we create 20 of them in our bodies anyway, that some of the finest foods on the planet (including caviar, wine and artisan hams) depend on them, that essential vitamins have E numbers and that they are all around us, whether we like them or not. And 99.995% of every breath we take is a soup of Es.

Unless you've read a fair amount of the clinical research in this area, there's a strong possibility that everything you thought about Es *might* be wrong. I don't mean to sound patronising – I'm just basing this on the state of my own understanding before beginning properly to research the subject five years ago, and I'd say that 99% of what I thought about Es was wrong, and was based on what I'd heard from media nutritionists and hearsay. Not only was it wrong but, in retrospect, a lot was illogical, paranoid and a little hysterical. You see, in order to understand if something is bad for you to eat, you have to start off by accepting a paradox:

'Every edible substance on the planet can kill you. The best thing you can do is to eat as wide a range of different edible substances as possible.'

Toxicology is the study of poisons*, and the father of toxicology is considered to be a chap called Paracelsus, who lived from 1493 to 1541. He is famous for summing up the essence of his subject with this quote:

> *'All things are poison and nothing is without poison; only the dose makes a thing not a poison.'*

It's impossible to say that Es are safe, seeing as everything can kill you at a high enough dose. So let's be absolutely clear: Yes, E numbers can kill you, but so could apples, apricots, potatoes and rhubarb. Even water can kill if you drink too much of it. In 2008 a 40-year-old British woman called Jacqueline Henson died from water intoxication after drinking four litres of water in less than two hours as part of a weight-loss diet**.

I tell you this not to shock you, but to reassure you, because the solution is in the one piece of decent advice that you are highly unlikely to hear from any pill-touting holistic nutritionist on the TV but is the one that most clinical dietitians, GPs and gastroenterologists espouse... enjoy your food, try to eat as broad a range of foods as you can, don't eat too much and cook for yourself whenever you can.

Parts of this book may give you the impression that I am an unquestioning admirer of the food industry. That's not the case. I am well aware of iniquitous, bullying food industry malpractice and multinational mendacity, and the supermarkets that sell their products are to blame for a fair few problems, too. I'd be a fool if I didn't imagine that the £173 billion we spent last year on food, drink and catering wasn't a temptation too strong for some dodgy operators to cut corners and get consumed by competitive advantage. But the E number system is one regulatory mechanism that helps to avoid malpractice rather than encourages it. And even though I moan about the lengthening food chain, monopolistic supermarkets, food waste, crap packaging, dodgy marketing and horrible over-processed junk, am I really the only person in the country who's also quietly impressed by a system that manages to grow, process, and distribute enough food to allow our 62 million population to eat three meals every single day?

Neither do I advocate that you eat Es whenever you can. In the course of my research for this book I've tasted lots of crap, disgusting foods that

---

* Or, more specifically, the study of the adverse effects of chemicals on living organisms.
** http://news.bbc.co.uk/1/hi/england/bradford/7779079.stm

have been made with Es, and a fair amount of cheap and nasty food is only technologically possible because of E numbers. But what about my delicious wines, hams and cakes that are also made technologically possible by E numbers? Why is it fine if we eat additives but not when other people do? And who am I to tell anyone that they shouldn't eat food simply because it's cheap or because I don't like it? I enjoy eating Wotsits and processed cheese slices as my guilty food pleasures, for crying out loud.

If this introduction sounds a bit defensive, it's because I've had so many arguments with people about writing this book. As soon as I say that E numbers don't seem to be as bad as we thought, people get angry and talk of mendacious food manufacturers, hyperactivity, cancer and growth hormones in cattle (which aren't E numbers, incidentally), yet most can't define what an E actually is. We hold many nutritional fallacies to be rock-solid, mainly because they are so often repeated in the media. I hope that this book will help breathe some fresh air and fascination into the stale and sorry state of our – and our children's – nutrition. Perhaps it will give you a new perspective on your diet and help you tackle the more important health issues in your daily life. We shouldn't be afraid of Es. We should understand them.

Cooking with E numbers

All of our favourite food writers use E numbers in their food, although they rarely – if ever – say that the ingredients they list are Es. Delia Smith's *How to Cheat at Cooking* is a veritable festival of Es as she suggests very specific brands and products containing Es such as Hartley's orange and lime-flavoured jellies (E330, E331, E260, E100, E120, E160a, E141), Baxter's Lobster bisque (E452), Jus-Rol pastry (E471), Aunt Bessie's Homestyle Roast Potatoes (E100, E160c) and Tesco's Piri Piri peppers (E270 – lactic acid) to name but a few.

Hugh Fearnley-Whittingstall's *River Cottage Cookbook* recipe for Elderflower Cordial includes tartaric acid, although he omits to say that this is also known as E334. His recipe for curing hams lists saltpetre in the ingredients. He points out that this is sodium nitrate but doesn't mention its E number (E251).

Nigella Lawson loves two Es in particular. Flicking through her *How to be a Domestic Goddess*, she makes ample use of E500 (sodium bicarbonate) and E450 (one of several diphosphates), the components of baking powder, used for so many of her wonderful recipes. She suggests using dolly mixtures and pink food colouring (both almost inevitably using E120, cochineal, E122 Carmoisine and E110, Sunset Yellow). Every recipe that needs self-raising flour is asking you to add E500 (sodium bicarbonate) and usually E341 (calcium phosphate).

Heston Blumenthal uses E330 (citric acid) and sodium bicarbonate too, although often to regulate pH, see *Perfection*, page 286.

What is
an E number?

E numbers are what identify the 319 food additives approved for a specific use in Europe.

That's the short answer, but don't worry, the longer explanation isn't complicated and can be boiled down to a few bullet points:

- The E stands for Europe.
- Approval is recommended to the European Commission by the EFSA (European Food Safety Authority), which analyses the research into additives, sets acceptable levels of them and gives specific details about what they can and cannot be used for (sweeteners are not allowed in baby foods, for example).
- They are constantly being reassessed and some have been withdrawn from food use (e.g. E103 and E105), others added.
- They have many different uses. The most important are colours, preservatives, stabilizers, gelling agents, acidity regulators, flavour enhancers and sweeteners.
- Some additives are naturally occurring and others are manufactured by the chemical industry.

But wait, there's more:

– Our bodies naturally create 20 different E number compounds, whether or not the food that we eat contains them. There are Es in our blood, fat, sweat, semen and hair.

– Or bodies contain over 90 different E compounds sourced from natural unprocessed food.

– 47 Es are approved for use in organic food (which means food can contain these and still qualify as 'organic').

– There are actually 507 E numbers in total, but many of them are only for use in cosmetics, for example.

– You could apply for your very own E number to be authorized, if you fancy it. Just send a letter and a technical dossier to:
European Commission Health and Consumer Directorate-General Directorate E – Safety of the food chain Unit E3 – Chemicals, Contaminants, Pesticides Office B232, 4/49, B-1049 Brussels.
You may need to wait a few years for an answer, mind.

– An EU-approved additive doesn't have to be listed on a label by its E number – packs can give their real name instead. This is not helpful. (I've included an A–Z of names at the back of this book if you want to look any up.)

– If you want to be nit-picking, EU legislation defines food additives as 'any substance not normally consumed as a food in itself and not normally used as a characteristic ingredient of food, whether or not it has nutritive value, the intentional addition of which to food for a technological purpose results in it or its by-products becoming directly or indirectly a component of such foods'. There is a strict and onerous system of Byzantine rules, regulations and directives controlling how and why they are used in all manner of foods that goes into minute detail.

– For instance, this is from the European Parliament and Council Directive No 95/2/EC (Yes, I actually read these things): 'The substances listed under numbers E400, E401, E402, E403, E404, E406, E407, E407a, E410, E412, E413, E414, E415, E417, E418 and E440 may not be used in jelly mini-cups, defined, for the purpose of this Directive, as jelly confectionery of a firm consistency, contained in semi-rigid mini-cups or mini-capsules, intended to be ingested in a single bite by exerting pressure on the mini-cups or mini-capsule to project the confectionery into the mouth.'

16

Are E numbers chemicals?

Yes. But then *everything* we eat or drink is a chemical, or more accurately, a soup of chemicals. A glass of water is a collection of chemicals – mostly hydrogen and oxygen bound together as H_2O. You may think that the air that you breathe is pretty basic stuff, but it's also another soup of chemicals – nitrogen, oxygen, argon and small proportions of others, most of which happen to have E numbers (see page 26).

What are they made from?

Some are naturally occurring organic substances that are milled or distilled, such as E412 (guar gum, used to control the texture of yoghurts and ice creams), which is simply the dehusked, milled and screened seeds of the guar bean, mainly grown in India and Pakistan. Others are synthetic, which means that they are created by chemical reactions such as heating, fermentation, dissolution, distillation, etc.

E150a is plain caramel, made by the heating of carbohydrates (e.g. sugars), usually together with acids, alkalis or salts, E160c is an extract of paprika, E100 refined turmeric. E101, riboflavin, also known as vitamin B2 (a key micronutrient added to cereals for health reasons and also used as a food colour), is made in several different ways including the biosynthesis of various organisms such as bacteria and fungi. Basically, the fungi and bacteria produce the E101 as a by-product. E124 (Ponceau 4R, red food colouring) is synthesized from coal tar.

Some are more surprising, such as E120 (cochineal), which is made of the crushed and refined casings of the cochineal insect, which lives on cacti and is mainly produced in South America. The notorious E621 (MSG or monosodium glutamate) is usually made from sugar beet or molasses. The carbohydrates in them are fermented using yeasts to create MSG. Others are created by multiple reactions that are complex and mind-boggling, but a little too dull and long-winded for a pithy, myth-busting popular science book.

Why are Es in my food?

Most Es are in food to stop it going off, to make it taste, look or feel better in your mouth, for dietary reasons (e.g. vitamins and low-calorie sweeteners) or give it a longer shelf-life. The rules state that Es must 'perform a useful purpose, are safe and do not mislead the consumer'.

The main categories are:

Colours

Ever wondered why M&Ms are so colourful? The ones I'm munching on now (just for the purposes of research, I promise you) have E100 (yellow-orange), E120 (pink/purple), E133 (red/blue), E160e (orange-red), E171 (white). Some say that artificial colours are merely cosmetic and therefore unnecessary, but it's not that simple. We make important choices based on the appearance of food, and colour performs important psychological functions, altering our perception of the taste.

If you doubt the power of colour, try this experiment: I asked a group of experienced wine enthusiasts to taste a white Pinot Gris wine to which I had added red dye, followed by that exact same wine unadulterated. *Everyone* in the group was fooled, guessing red grape varieties and talking of blackcurrant notes, fruit and tannins. They described the white entirely differently, using classic white wine flavour references. Make no mistake, colour directly influences our taste perceptions, and as such it will control nutrition by informing our food choices.

Preservatives

Nitrates and nitrites are in most bacon. They guard against botulism (the most powerful toxin on the planet) and help retain the red colour of meat. Without it, food would have a shorter shelf life, probably be more expensive and we would be much more likely to die from food poisoning.

Antioxidants

These stop food from rotting or turning brown, and stop fats from turning rancid. When you pop a lemon in a bowl of cut apples to stop them going brown, you are adding an antioxidant.

Sweeteners

Pretty self-explanatory, this one. You'll find these in diet or low-calorie drinks, as most of them are, weight-for-weight, much sweeter (often several hundred times sweeter), yet lower in calories and safer for teeth than natural sugar.

Emulsifiers, stabilizers, thickeners and gelling agents

Emulsifiers like lecithin help ingredients such as oil and water to mix together when they would otherwise separate, as in mayonnaise. Although not strictly emulsifiers, stabilizers often have the same effect, stopping ingredients from separating. Gelling agents are substances like pectin, which are in jams to make them set, and can also work as a substitute for fats in low-calorie foods.

How much E can I eat?

The WHO (World Health Organization) usually uses a safety margin of at least 100 when determining the safe levels (Acceptable Daily Intake or ADI) of additives. Basically they work out the amount of any additive that an animal can eat without having any bad effects, then divide it by 10 (in case a human is x10 times more sensitive than an animal) and then this figure is divided by 10 again to account for a range of sensitivities in humans. Essentially, a safe level has been found, and then divided by 100 just to be sure. Even then, food manufacturers are only allowed to use a fraction of that ADI on the assumption that you may eat many products containing that same additive in the course of a normal day.*

In practise, this is a bloody good thing, because it's extremely difficult to find out how much of any E number is in a product. I called up Mars to find out how much of my ADI of the colours I was eating in my M&Ms and they took seven days to get back to me. They finally said 'The information you have requested is not standard information that we would give out as it involves sensitive recipe data.' I would have followed it up, but I'd finished my M&Ms by then.

Going a little deeper: the lists of Es and their ADIs are actually only a small part of the legislation – there are a huge variety of rules that define how they can be used, and there are lots of foods that aren't allowed to contain any of them, or are restricted to only containing certain ones. For instance JEFCA (the Joint Food and Agriculture/World Health Organization's Executive Committee on Food Additives) advises that sulphur dioxide E220 has an ADI of 0–0.7 milligrams per kg of body weight (so basically, if you weigh 70 kilos, you should consume no more than 49mg a day). When it's present in food, the producer has to take into account how much of that ADI will be used up by their product, even if you eat or drink it to excess (and seeing as E220 is in almost every bottle of wine, they need to keep the amounts pretty low. Aspartame has an ADI of 0–40 milligrams per kg of body weight. By contrast, MSG

---

* http://www.inchem.org/documents/ehc/ehc/ehc70.htm

(E621) is considered so safe that it doesn't even have an ADI, and many have the advice 'Quantum satis' which simply means you should only use as much of it as you need, and no more, to perform a specific function. If that seems a bit vague for you, it may come as some succour that most Es have a tightly restricted list of foods in which they can be used, so it's not as though they are scattered in foods by the bucketful whether they are needed or not. The details are here:

http://www.food.gov.uk/ multimedia/pdfs/guidance.pdf

The ADIs for all the E Numbers are currently undergoing review – many of the limits date back to suggestions made in 1995 and our eating habits change, so if we are habitually eating more of one type of food or drink (perhaps everyone goes cherryade mad), the levels in them need to change accordingly. The current ADI review is starting with colours (specifically with the Southampton Six, see page 46) and is expected to be finished in 2020.

An E poisoning experiment

I thought it only fair to spend 24 hours seeing if I could harm myself by overeating on crap, processed food. I bought £100 worth of products that listed the most Es on their labels: doughy frozen pizzas, crisps, luncheon meat, chicken poppets (hoh, yes), instant noodles and high-energy drinks. The idea was to see if I could overdose on Es. Why was this food crap? Because it tasted bloody awful. Most products were very high in salt, leaving me with a sore, stinging sensation in my mouth after eating my first few meals, and by the end of the day I felt sore, sick, bloated and miserable.

Two weeks later I visited Dr Jonty Heaversedge, an NHS GP, who looked at the amount of food I'd eaten in a single day and professed himself appalled (although I suspect he was actually quite impressed). He had worked out the statistics of what I'd eaten: 8,500 calories of horrible food (nearly four times the recommended amount) and 50 E number additives. He had worked out how much of each E I had eaten and analysed whether or not I had put myself in danger.

Trouble was, I hadn't. 32 of the Es I ate were so untoxic that they didn't even have upper limits of daily consumption, and I had only gone over my ADI on one additive: nitrates in various forms, and that by a whopping 700%. But interestingly, Jonty wasn't at all concerned about my consumption of Es, or even the nitrates (the safety margins on the ADIs of nitrates are so high that I was nowhere near dangerous levels), but by the sheer scale of my fat, salt and sugar intake, none of which have E numbers. If I ate food like that on a long-term basis I was likely to be looking at obesity, heart disease and circulatory problems very quickly.

There's little doubt that a lot of processed food can be relatively high in fat, salt and sugar, and that this poses a huge health risk if you eat it to the exclusion of fresh fruit and vegetables. But the problems posed by crap food are often little to do with their E numbers.

What *isn't* an E number?

People like picking fights with me over my defence of (some) Es, and they are right to do so; if I'm going to say something that outrages them, I should expect to take some flak. But they often argue with me about substances that *aren't* Es, so at the risk of sounding snide, here are a few of them:

Flavourings – Whether artificial or not, these don't have E numbers and they are controlled by different laws to other food additives, and although a label must say if they are in a product, they don't need to be listed.

Caffeine – It may be an addictive psychoactive stimulant drug proven to cause anxiety, muscle twitching, insomnia, mania, depression and headaches, but an E number it is not. On balance it's probably best not to consume it, but at the same time I should add that *they'll take my coffee out of my cold, dead hands.*

Cattle growth hormones – Monsanto's *Posilac* is the best known of these and it's given to cows to increase milk yield (which it does by around 10–16%). About 17% of US cows are on bovine growth hormones and they are associated with potential (although disputed) cancer fears in humans and some grim animal health problems such as lameness and mastitis. They aren't, however, Es.

Salt – There is a small but highly significant increase in risk of stroke and cardiovascular disease from long-term high salt intake, although a lack of salt in our diet can be fatal too. If you eat a lot of processed food, it's probably a good idea to be very careful, but seeing as I hate culinary paranoia I should add that if you cook most of your own food rather than eating processed food, you may get nowhere near the FSA's recommendation of a maximum of 6g of salt per day.

If you've got some sensitive scales, pour out 6g of salt to take a good look at it (I think it's quite a lot – I'd love to know what you think). I've measured my daily salt usage when cooking fresh food, and it's usually around 2–3g, even though I like my food well seasoned. But the moment you add processed food like bacon, shop-bought bread, sandwiches and salads with dressing – you're adding salt. But it's not an E number.

Incidentally, if salt (or chocolate, for that matter) were to apply for an E number it would be unlikely to get one due to the health implications (feed enough chocolate to a lab rat and it will die; E number application refused). On the other hand, if it did have an E number, it could be properly controlled by food regulations and any problems it causes could be eradicated. We might be fractionally healthier, although I for one would be much unhappier.

Mechanically Recovered Meat (MRM) – While many MRM products may contain Es, this unappetising meat slurry is not an E.

Sugar – Poses problems by sheer calorific value, problematic for diabetics, and causes tooth decay. It is not an E, and not limited in our food.

Hydrogenated fats – Hydrogenation is used to turn a liquid fat like vegetable oil into a solid fat as in margarine (hydrogen is added to the oil and some unsaturated fatty acids are converted to saturated ones). It is not an E number, and despite the hysteria, its now rarely found in UK foods.

Trans fats – or partially hydrogenated fats, can be found in some hydrogenated vegetable oils and at low levels in meat and dairy products. Trans fats are banned in Denmark and New York City, although in the UK we only eat a around 2.5g of them every day (half the maximum recommended amount).

All about Es

Good Es?

Food manufacturers use some artificial additives simply to make products look better than they really are, or to give them a competitive advantage that they might or might not pass on to the consumer. Sometimes they create cheap, rubbish food and sell it to us at a large mark-up. However not all processed food is rubbish (my holy trinity of wine, ham and cheese, for example), and some Es have some surprisingly useful healthy functions.

Disease: Remove the E numbered vitamins and minerals from cereals and other foods and at least some of us are likely to pay the consequences: beriberi, scurvy and rickets. Removing nitrate and nitrite preservatives (some of the more controversial E numbers) from pork products would significantly increase the risk of botulism – a pathogen that has been all but eradicated from our food.

Many anti-E campaigners note quite rightly that botulism is now a rare disease, but that's partly because nitrates have been used in cured pork products for hundreds of years – well before they were given their E number (Hannah Glasse advised to add a pound of salt-peter – potassium nitrate – to a hog in 1748). Dr Kathie Grant, a microbiologist at the Health Protection Agency's Centre for Diseases is very concerned indeed about botulism and showed me some of it in a Petri dish, explaining that a teaspoon of the toxin would be enough to kill the entire population of the UK.

Nutrition: What would happen if, say, we had to live entirely without all those vitamin and mineral Es? Many essential vitamins would be off the menu: vitamin C (E300), vitamin E (306–9), vitamin B2 (E101). There's a danger that beriberi, scurvy and rickets could start making a comeback (a complete lack of vitamin C can kill you from scurvy within 4–6 weeks).

We do get a lot of minerals and vitamins from our diets without them *having* to be added to foods, but the people who are most likely to suffer when you remove them would not be the middle classes, who generally eat pretty well and can afford to adapt to buy fresh foods, it would be the poor, the frail and the elderly, all of whom already live on something of a nutritional knife-edge. Three million people in the UK are considered to suffer from – or be at risk of – malnutrition. These will be the ones most likely to pay the consequences in terms of beriberi, scurvy and rickets if vitamins and minerals aren't added to food.

If you need to eat low-fat, low-salt, low-sugar or low-calorie food (or if you're a diabetic) or you don't have the time or skills to make it yourself, you may need to buy food that has been specially tailored to your nutritional requirements, and that food is likely to include more artificial additives in order to give the texture and taste that it would otherwise lack. Sugars already provide about 20% of the energy intake in the USA. Why shouldn't people cut down on their sugar calorie intake if they want to?

Artificial sweeteners such as aspartame, saccharin and acesulfame, etc. may provoke ridicule amongst gourmands, but they play an important role in calorie control, in foods for diabetic conditions, and their use as sugar-replacements helps avoid a significant amount of tooth decay. All of these can have a positive effect on our health and their use can save billions of pounds on health services.

Sunflower spread is often a veritable cocktail of E numbers, including colours and preservatives. Now, I'm not an enormous fan of margarines and spreads, and like most people I love saturated fat foods, but since Dr Jonty took me aside and told me I have dangerously high cholesterol levels, I view such spreads with less of a sneer. Sunflower spreads might need artificial additives in to make them appealing, but it's 78% lower in saturated fats than butter, so it can help you to manage your health. Personally, I'm planning to cut back on my weekly cheese mountain before turning to Flora, but I'm not going to criticize anyone who does.

Without MSG and other flavour enhancers processed foods would almost certainly be made with more salt, which would lead to increased risks of heart disease, strokes and higher blood pressure. So we demonize these foods at our own risk because, if food manufacturers are forced to do without additives, there may be health consequences we weren't expecting.

The price of food: This would rise significantly if manufacturers couldn't control its stability or longevity with Es and this would have direct consequences on nutrition. I'm sure that food companies squeeze every penny of profit that they can from us. Even so, food is a highly competitive market, so they often need to pass savings on otherwise consumers will buy other cheaper products. Many people will buy on price as much, if not more so, as on quality, which is a shame but true.

There are lots of reasons why cheap food damages the environment, farmers and workers. At the same time, however, the people who would suffer nutritionally from more expensive food are likely to be the elderly, the sick and the poorest 20% of British people, who spend around one-third of their income on food. A rise in prices of food for this group would – and does – cause real hardship, and results in them buying less food, or cheaper, less nutritious products. These people are already nutritionally vulnerable, and this is probably the last thing they need. Actually, what they *really* need is the knowledge and enthusiasm to make better, cheaper, fresh food for themselves, but until this miracle happens, processed food is here to stay.

Convenience: Without preservatives food spoils more quickly and without antioxidants foods turn brown quicker and fats in them become rancid more quickly. So 'buy smaller amounts of fresh food and shop more frequently' you might think, but we should be wary of denigrating convenience as simple laziness: many elderly, less well-off or busy people can't or won't shop frequently, some also have little or rare access to decent shops, so longer-life foods significantly improve their lives.

Sensory perception and pleasure: Many anti-E commentators dismiss artificial additives as merely cosmetic. But if you don't think that food should be anything other than its constituent parts, why do we eat a chocolate mousse when you could simply eat chocolate and cream? Why have ice cream when you could have cream? Why freeze anything? In fact, why not liquidize every meal – it'll help your digestion, after all.

Most of us go to great lengths to make foods look wonderful, and I don't believe that's irrelevant. Why is it OK for one person to add a tad of saffron or a spoonful of turmeric and a teeny sprig of chervil to a fine dinner party meal, but not for someone to enjoy a microwave curry containing annatto and paprika extract that make it look comforting? Why is one person's foie gras pâté (with a vast saturated fat load) a creamy delight, yet another's low-cal supper bulked up with carrageenan (to give it body without calories) a culinary travesty? Aren't veloutés, foams, timbales, jellies, millefeuilles and myriad garnishes *cosmetic*? Let's not forget that eating is a sensory experience and that enjoying eating is an immensely important part of our lives, whether it's because a food's colour reassures us or delights us. These cosmetic issues are important and tangible.

Taste: Without sulphur dioxide wine tastes foul. Without acidity regulators many drinks would lose their sharpness and tang. My daughters' homemade Daisy & Poppy Elderflower Cordial will cease to exist without ascorbic acid and their classmates won't get their spring presents.

Additives as cooking tools: Without the E500 (sodium bicarbonate) together with E450(i) (disodium diphosphate) in baking powder, cakes won't rise and children will cry. I rest my case.

Natural Es

Let's just take a few moments to imagine a world without E numbers so we can understand how much better it is with them. Let's remove all substances that have E numbers from the planet and see what happens. Hold your breath…

Actually, you'd better hold your breath for a very long time, because 99.995% of the air that we breathe is E numbers. It's 78% nitrogen (E941), 21% oxygen (E948), 0.93% argon (E938), 0.04% carbon dioxide (E290) 0.0018% neon (which, shockingly enough, isn't approved for food use), 0.0005% helium (E939) and a few others in tiny percentages.

But let's assume that you can hold your breath forever, or that you develop the ability to breathe exclusively neon, and sit down to a nice meal. It will be a pretty meagre meal because most foods contain naturally occurring versions of E numbers that are found in our food, whether it's fresh, organic or processed to hell. Imagine what life would be like without the following…

Tomatoes contain seven E substances: glutamate – also known as E621 (monosodium glutamate), carotene (E160a), lycopene (E160d), riboflavin (E101), ascorbic acid (E300), citric acid (E330) and malic acid (E296).

Apples contain 11 E substances: riboflavin (E101), carotene (E160a), anthocyanin (E163), acetic acid (E260), vitamin C (E300), citric acid (E330), tartaric acid (E334), pectin (E440), succinic acid (E363), glutamic acid (E620) and cysteine (E920).

These facts alone don't make either Es or tomatoes any better or any worse, but perhaps when we understand that a lot of these substances are around us in nature, we can feel a little less scared and a little more prepared to accept them. It doesn't sound very romantic, I'll admit, but once we accept that as well as being the tools of one of the most sensual crafts at mankind's disposal (cooking), all ingredients are also chemicals, perhaps we can overcome some of the hysteria that gets in the way of our understanding of nutrition.

Of course, because all of these substances in tomatoes and apples haven't been *added*, they aren't classed as E numbers and don't have to be listed on a label. But they still perform the same functions, and are metabolized by our bodies in the same way.

Here's a *very* small sample of naturally occurring sources of Es:

Apples, oranges and jams contain pectin (E440).
Beetroots: Beetroot Red (E162) comes from beets.
Bread: wheat naturally contains riboflavin (E101) amongst others.
Caramel: E150a.
Carrots, spinach, pumpkins, mangoes and sweet potatoes: beta-carotene (E160a).
Cranberries: benzoic acid (E210).
Blackcurrants, red peppers, parsley, broccoli, strawberries, oranges, lemons, melons, cauliflowers, garlic, potatoes, grapes, carrots, avocados, apples, lettuce and cucumbers: vitamin C (E300).
Paprika: paprika extract (E160c).
Parmesan cheese, cured hams, cheddar cheese, scallops, asparagus, peas, onions, roast chicken, beef and pork: all contain free glutamate, which is essentially a naturally occurring version of MSG (E621). This list is in descending order of concentration – Parmesan cheese has the second-highest concentration of glutamate of any common food after konbu, a seaweed used as a flavouring in Japanese food.

Tomatoes: cellulose, glutamates or flavour enhancer E621 (monosodium glutamate), colours E160a, carotene, E160d lycopene, E101 riboflavin, antioxidant E300 (ascorbic acid), acids E330 (citric acid), E296 (malic acid), (oxalic acid) and flavourings*.

Tuna: inosinate (naturally-occurring version of E630/632/633, E628 and E629).

Vinegar: acetic acid E260.

Wine, tea: tannin E181.

How Es saved our lives

If you think that there was a halcyon era before E numbers, when Ye Olde Britain was awash with good, honest free-range food made with natural flavours and colours, produced by conscientious farmers and sold by grocers who cared about customers over profits…think again. Toxicologists say that the E number system has saved hundreds of thousands of lives and stopped hundreds of thousands more from dying early, mainly because the system *prohibits* the use of some terrible additives of the past, many of which could be very nasty indeed.

Dr Lisa Ackerley (Professor of Environmental Health at Salford University) says that, 'Without the legislative infrastructure to control food safety, without the Environmental Health and Trading Standards Officers, the Food Standards Agency and Health Protection Agency, we would be no further forward than in the nineteenth century. A system of E numbers is better than no system at all. These days, consumers have a choice – they can see what is on the label and decide for themselves. In the past, they were none the wiser, and suffered sometimes-horrific consequences of consuming poisonous food.

'The migration of workers from country to town during the industrial revolution changed the process by which food moved from farm to fork. From once being responsible for growing their own food, these migrants

---

* Heinz states the following on the label of its tomato ketchup: 'Naturally contains lycopene (8.5mg per 100g)'. Whilst this openness in labelling is to be applauded, I wonder if this shred of information actually causes confusion, because the label doesn't say what lycopene (which, if it was added to ketchup, would have to be listed as E160d) is or does, how much of it you are advised to consume in a day, or why they have decided to draw our attention to it. In fact, it's a powerful antioxidant so it might help fight disease and there is some evidence that lycopene helps fight cancer. This is so inconclusive that in 2005 the USFDA only allowed the following claim on tomatoes and tomato products to ensure that consumers aren't misled: 'Very limited and preliminary scientific research suggests that eating one-half to one cup of tomatoes and/or tomato sauce a week may reduce the risk of prostate cancer. FDA concludes that there is little scientific evidence supporting this claim.'

in cities now relied on others to supply food to them. Food became a commodity – dilution of food with cheaper and sometimes dangerous substances was a means of increasing profit. Shelf-life became an issue as food was transported in large quantities from source to place of consumption, and more additives became necessary and, uncontrolled, became another form of adulteration of food.'

Before the E number system came along, British food was pretty grim. I have vivid memories of the 1970s and how foul food was then (butter was a rare delicacy in my house, straw-tasting frozen economy burgers a staple), but it gets worse. Malnutrition was still a devastating problem in Britain as recently as the 1950s and we have only recently eradicated many diseases caused by nutritional deficiencies, such as scurvy, pellagra, goitre, rickets, beriberi and iron-deficiency anemia. But it gets far, far worse – and more dangerous – the further back you go. Here are a few of the worst food adulterations of the good old days before E number regulations:

Milk: was regularly watered down until modern controls came into force. This would invariably be done not just by the farmers but also by the middlemen and sellers, and after watering down it would often be coloured yellow using lead chromate (especially in USA) to make it appear more creamy. This would lead to lead poisoning.

Cream: was also watered down by unscrupulous suppliers, but could still be used to make whipped cream if you added raw cows' brains. I managed to recreate this experiment using raw pigs' brains, and it does indeed make a lovely silky-smooth stiff foam.

Flour: Dust was regularly swept from bakery floors and mixed back in with the raw flour.

Tea: was one of the most frequently adulterated foodstuffs as it was a luxury import. Old tea leaves would sometimes be recycled by being boiled with ferrous sulphate and sheep's dung, coloured with Prussian blue (ferric ferrocyanide), verdigris (copper acetate), logwood, tannin or lampblack before being resold. New tea was often bulked up by being adulterated with gypsum (a cheap white chalky substance) and soot (to keep the colour).

Children's sweets: In the early 1800s, Red Lead (lead tetroxide) was added to children's sweets to make them bright orangey-red. It's highly toxic, and caused lead poisoning (abdominal pain, anaemia and coma were symptoms, with death fairly common). When I borrowed a pot of it to show what it looks like, I had to wear a face mask and surgical gloves to handle it, and it had to be disposed of by a specialist toxic waste company. A study of 100 sweets sold in Britain during this period found that 59 contained lead chromate, 12 contained Red Lead and 10 contained Brunswick Green (a mixture of Prussian Blue and lead chromate).

Copper colouring: Green vegetables would often be boiled in a copper pan in order to keep them vividly green. While doing this, the copper in the pan would also help to poison the diner. Acute cases after high consumption result in a wide variety of gruesome symptoms.

Lead: saucepans were used by the wealthy to cook apples. The lead leeching into the apples would intensify their sweetness but, again, the joys of lead poisoning would come your way. Lancashire dairies heated milk up in lead pans and mint for mint salad was ground using a giant ball of lead that left lead deposits in the herbs.

Cyanide: Leaves of cherry laurel were often added to custard to capture the bitter, nutty taste of almonds without the cost. It's a shame that they contain large amounts of cyanide. I rather stupidly tried some – they do indeed have an excellent bitter tang.

Beer: was often adulterated to toxic levels to give it a good tang. In 1790 Samuel Child wrote a book on making beer including ingredients that contained strychnine and vitriol (sulphuric acid). There's nothing wrong with sulphuric acid in the right hands and used according to proper regulations (it has an E number, E513 after all), but in the hands of a brewer back then it was often highly dangerous.

So what was done about it?

1771 *'The bread I eat in London is a deleterious paste, mixed up with chalk, alum and bone ashes, insipid to the taste and destructive to the constitution. The good people are not ignorant of this adulteration; but they prefer it to wholesome bread, because it is whiter than the meal of corn [wheat]. Thus they sacrifice their taste and their health. . . to a most absurd gratification of a misjudged eye; and the miller or the baker is obliged to poison them and their families, in order to live by his profession.'* Tobias Smollett, The Expedition of Humphry Clinker

1820 The London-based chemist Friedrich Accum, concerned about food safety, publishes his *A Treatise on Adulterations of Food and Culinary Poisons*, denouncing many dangerous chemical additives in food, naming names of the worst swindlers and poisoners, and earning himself the ire and threats of many food fiddlers.

1850 Sir Charles Wood speaks in Parliament about the adulteration of coffee with chicory. It wasn't dangerous, but the discovery of a technique to test for adulteration led to the first Food Adulteration Act of 1860, laying down the foundations of food regulation in this country.

1885 Coca-Cola began life as a stimulating 'medicinal' cocktail made with cocaine and a hefty wallop of caffeine from kola nuts.

1960s The tide of public opinion turns – finally bright vivid colours are not seen as an absolute virtue and people become rightly wary of unregulated food additives.

1964 The first really practical laws regulating food begin to be written, starting with the Meat (Treatment) Regulations, and followed over the next 20 years by laws covering other foods and additives.

1968 In a massive scandal in Italy, 174 men and women connected to the popular Vino Ferrari wine company are charged with adulterating or faking wine, and 10,000 tons of fake wine are seized. A recipe quoted in an Italian court: 'Crush the pulp and stone of dates in a container, mix with hot water, clarify with lead acetate, add sugar to the mixture, then add chloridic acid. Heat to 60 or 70ºC. Let cool immediately and neutralize with potash.'

1984 Food Labelling Regulations finally ensure at least some level of openness on what's in the food you buy. Also, Maurice Hanssen publishes *E for Additives*, the first popular food additive guide, shocking the UK public.

1984 The Food Act delivers a comprehensive framework for the implementation and interpretation of food regulations.

1987 In the US, the Beech-Nut Nutrition Corporation pays $2.2m for violating the Federal Food Drug and Cosmetic Act by selling artificially flavoured sugar water as apple juice.

2002 The European Food Safety Authority (EFSA) is established. Based in Parma, Italy, its role is 'to assess and communicate on all risks associated with the food chain'.

2008 Milk in China is found to be contaminated with melamine, and infant formula from it kills at least 6 children and harms an estimated 300,000 more. China executes two of the people involved. It's not an E number, but serves to heighten fear of them anyway.

Nature good: science bad?

Remember me saying that every food on the planet can kill you? Well, I can understand if you don't really believe this yet, so take a look at these interesting components lurking in some fresh unadulterated foods: naturally occurring toxins, carcinogens and mutagens that *could* kill you if you ate enough of them. Brace yourself, because this may put you (very briefly) off your lunch.

Alfalfa sprouts contain the toxin *canavanine*.

Apples contain a cyanide and sugar compound called *amygdalin* in their pips. It's a poison that can kill by asphyxiation.

Apricots also contain cyanide in the form of *amygdalin*, especially in the kernels.

Bananas contain *5-hydroxytryptamine* that can cause hallucinations.

Bread contains the carcinogens *urethane* and *allyl isothiocyanate* and the tumorigen *ethyl carbamate*. Wheat can contain *altertoxins*.

Broccoli contains the carcinogen *allyl isothiocyanate*.

Cabbages contain *goitrogens* that cause thyroid damage, *allyl isothiocyanate*, a dangerous toxic lachrymator (the common component of tear gas —I've tasted a few different versions of tear gas and none of them are particularly agreeable). *Isothiocyanates* are the substances that make mustard, horseradish and wasabi so fiery – in fact the most accurate way to describe what tear gas feels like is to imagine a wasabi overdose.

Carrots contain the toxin *furocoumarin*.

Cassava contains *cyanogenic glycosidei* in high doses. It must be dried, soaked and baked to be rendered harmless.

Celery contains *furocoumarin*.

Chicken, when grilled, contains carcinogenic *nitropyrenes*.

Chips contain *acrylamide*, a potentially dangerous chemical formed during the cooking of starchy foods, including potatoes and bread.

Coffee Oh dear – this contains all manner of fun including 19 rodent carcinogens. It contains *benzo(a)pyrene*, *hydrogen peroxide* and *tannin*, the mutagens *chlorogenic acid*, *diacetyl*, *methyl glyoxal* and toxic *caffeine*.

Kidney beans Red kidney bean poisoning is caused by the toxin *Phytohaemagglutinin* (kidney bean lectin). In raw beans the level of this toxin is so dangerous that just 5 beans can cause poisoning. The symptoms are nausea, vomiting and then diarrhoea. The toxin is all but destroyed by ten minutes of boiling.

Nutmeg contains *myristicin*, which can cause poisoning and is thought to be a strong deliriant.

Nuts: peanuts, maize and oilseeds, if poorly stored, can contain *aflatoxins*, some of the most carcinogenic substances ever identified.

Potatoes contain the glycoalkaloids *solanine* and *chaconine* that are concentrated in their leaves, sprouts and vines. Green potatoes indicate that they have increased glycoalkaloids (although the green colouring is from *chlorophyl*, which is harmless), and these toxins affect the nervous system.

Rhubarb leaves contain poisonous *oxalic acid*. There have been reports of deaths from rhubarb poisoning during World War II, although you'd have to eat a lot of leaves to reach LD50 (the median lethal dose which would kill 50% of consumers). While this is unlikely, it's still pretty toxic.

Shellfish toxins, again if badly stored, can cause *paralytic shellfish poisoning*, *diarrhetic shellfish poisoning* and several other horrors.

Tea contains the potentially carcinogenic compound *tannin*, which also makes you less able to absorb iron, which can lead to anaemia.

Toast when you've burnt it, is thought to contain benzo[*a*]pyrene, a potential carcinogen.

Water intoxication occurs when the level of electrolytes in the body drops dangerously low due to over-consumption of water. Water can be a poison just like any other substance.

So, what's the catch? The catch is that none of this should put you off natural foods because the nutritional benefits of eating all of the above outweigh the risks that, apart from rhubarb and kidney bean poisoning, are sometimes *tiny* (you'd need truckfuls of apples to poison yourself). My intention is merely to show that toxins occur throughout the natural world as well as the chemical world.

Extraordinary Es

For me, the most fascinating twist of the E numbers story is that a huge number of these substances exist in our bodies and the natural world without any food company interference, manufacture, synthesis or addition, and in foods that we see as entirely natural and unadulterated.

Human E numbers

A masked man hovers over me brandishing an absurd elephantine needle, about to plunge it into my abdomen. The moment is made ridiculous rather than scary by the sight of my visibly nauseous TV crew and the masked man's two absurdly gorgeous assistants, all of them wearing expressions of mild bewilderment (apart from poor Mario the soundman, who is facing the wall with his headphones turned down because he's not good with blood. He's decided to record this one by just watching the levels on his mixer, and I can't say I blame him). The masked man braces himself and plunges in. Oooooh that feels weird!

I'm writing this an hour after having liposuction to remove a small pot of fat from my tummy. The whole affair was a little more brutal and invasive than I was expecting, and I'm feeling oddly ashamed of myself, but the point of this exercise is to deconstruct and analyze my fat in order to isolate one of the E number compounds that naturally occur in the human body. In no way is it a lowbrow and humiliating attempt to shred what's left of my dignity in a desperate effort to boost our TV ratings. Anyway, I have a small pot of my fat in the fridge and the appropriate authorities have made no objection to me using it to isolate an E number substance it contains. They didn't strictly speaking say I couldn't cook a cake with it either, but that's probably because I didn't ask.

The body contains over 90 E number compounds, whether or not you have eaten them as additives in your food. Either your body synthesizes them from the food that you eat, or they can be extracted from everyday, E-free unprocessed food (as with ascorbic acid and essential fatty acids). Yes, you are basically a highly portable E-number factory. A lot of these substances play a part an essential role in the body's machinery and without them it simply wouldn't function.

The fact that these Es are natural doesn't in itself mean that they are any better or worse for you, but I hope that it might help to explain why we should understand Es rather than be afraid of them. And this is why Dr Mike Comins, a plastic surgeon who describes his normal line of work as 'body-sculpting' very kindly took 25cc of subcutaneous fat from me.

He started by injecting me with local anaesthetic, and then pumped my tummy full of a saline mixture including adrenaline. After about 20 minutes, he took out a gargantuan needle that would have terrified an elephant, and plunged it expertly but vigorously again and again through my navel into my belly while pulling on the plunger to extract the fat. Quite why it was such a shock baffles me – I had agreed to the whole thing in advance, but there you go. Mike handed me a plastic pot of my bright orange gloop and wished me luck with my experiment. I left the surgery slightly bemused but excited at the opportunities it offered, although minutes later, all that I could think of, was taking my sorry, sore (and fractionally lighter) body to bed.

A few days later I visited Professor Mike Batham at the Open University's chemistry lab in Milton Keynes to tear some of my bodily extracts apart and see if we could find the Es therein.

Human fat: E422 Glycerol

Glycerol is used as a humectant to keep foods, such as ready-made icing, moist during storage. There are lots of Es in human fat, but the glycerol seemed to be the one we were most likely to isolate.

I took my pot of man fat (which turns quite solid when it's put on ice) to Mike, who seemed remarkably unfazed by the sight of it. Maybe that's a chemist thing. We warmed the fat to make it liquid, then dissolved it using a strong solvent and separated off the resulting clear liquid. After adding salt (sodium chloride) to isolate our E number at the bottom of a test tube, we finally sucked out a thimbleful of glycerol. Joy.

Human hair: E920 L-cysteine

One of the real gross-out stories connected to Es is the Chinese factory that was busted for using human hair to create L-cysteine (although in the EU E920 is specifically *not* allowed to be made from human hair, it's estimated that more than 80% of cysteine used around the world comes from China, where it can be extracted from human hair and chicken feathers. The photos of the raid are gruesome, showing dirty-looking mounds of hair*, but this made me wonder if I could do the same – for personal use, you understand – because at 14% cysteine, hair is a particularly rich source of this amino acid. It's used in flour to help gluten relax and allow dough to mix well at high speeds, and also acts as a flavour enhancer (it's part of the magical Maillard reaction beloved of all chefs, whereby the browning of meats creates complex and delicious flavour compounds).

I had my hair cut in a blinding hurry by a chap called Sean, on my way back from filming in Sussex. We were running late for another interview, so halfway through the haircut the director told Sean to stop as we were running out of time. Everyone in the barber's shop sniggered as I left with half a hair cut (just around the sides, really), but I think it makes me look quite boyish. Anyway, when I took my hair to Mike in his lab, he first hydrolysed it in acid (breaking down the proteins), then added a solvent to extract the cysteine and some other amino acids, leaving two distinct layers. We then isolated the clearer liquid and heated it to evaporate everything except a few teaspoons of crystals, which were cysteine, alongside a few other amino acids left behind as impurities.

Sweat: E280 Propionic acid

This E is a saturated fatty acid normally found in human body fluids and excreted by our sweat glands (although for food use it's grown from lactic acid bacteria). It's used to stop bakery goods and cheeses from going mouldy, so it's perfect for my cake. It doesn't really need isolating – you just use a gas chromatography mass spectrometry (GCMS) test, calibrated to search for propionic acid and it shows up as a peak on a graph.

Tears: E1105 Lysozyme

Mike took a pot of tears I'd produced by holding some chopped onions in front of my nose, dropped a specially designed reagent into it and left

---

* http://www.cctv.com/news/financial/inland/20040104/100389_1.shtml

it to brew in an incubator for half an hour. We then looked at it under UV light, and the yellow glow revealed its presence. No need to extract it once we'd identified it there – I'll just use some neat tears in my cake.

Vomit: E507 Hydrochloric acid

The stomach is an extraordinary tool – it's tough enough to safely house a sack of highly corrosive hydrochloric acid (also used for pickling steel – basically eating the rust off it) without it leaking into the rest of the body, yet not dissolve itself. It creates hydrochloric acid as part of our gastric juices, alongside potassium chloride and sodium chloride (salt), which serve to start the digestive process. Hydrochloric acid is also E507, used for adjusting the pH of cheeses and in the production of gelatine.

I produced a good Tupperware box-full of vomit for the task, which was, oddly enough, more unpleasant than having invasive belly surgery (that nasty sourness in your mouth is the acid). Mike put it in a high-tech centrifuge that spun the vomit at 6,000 turns per second, separating it into three distinct layers – the heavy solids at the bottom, lighter ones at the top and the gastric juices including the hydrochloric acid in the middle. We checked the pH level of the liquid to determine its acidity (it was around 2.3 which is highly acidic) and added some silver nitrate to a splash of it, which went cloudy to show the presence of chloride in the solution. Together, these tests showed that we had hydrochloric acid.

My cake: So I made a cake with my own Es that I brought back from Mike's lab. It was a little pointless because, in a glorious twist of health and safety, I wasn't allowed to eat it due to the unsanitary conditions in Mike's chemistry lab and the high likelihood of cross-contamination from butanol and the like. The reality was that there wasn't any editorial reason to eat it anyway – any media broadcaster would rightly have slapped our wrists for that – but I was just intrigued as to what I'd make of the whole auto-cannibalism affair. I was a little devastated, but we'd proven the main facts: that you can extract Es from a human body.

Here are the others that you produce yourself, you magical thing, you:

E body counts

The following 20 Es are synthesized by your own body as part of its normal daily function:

E280	*Propionic acid*	E1105	*Lysozyme*
E322	*Lecithins*	E473	*Sucrose esters of fatty acids*
E1103	*Invertase*	E270	*Lactic acid*
E297	*Fumaric acid*	E325	*Sodium lactate*
E326	*Potassium lactate*	E330	*Citric acid*
E331	*Sodium citrates*	E332	*Potassium citrates*
E422	*Glycerol*	E507	*Hydrochloric acid*
E508	*Potassium chloride*	E509	*Calcium chloride*
E570	*Fatty acids*	E574	*Gluconic acid*
E620	*Glutamic acid*	E920	*L-cysteine hydrochloride*

And the following 96 Es are found in our bodies, sourced from natural, unprocessed food, whether or not that food has had any E numbers added to it.

E101(i)	*Riboflavin*	(ii)	*Riboflavin-5'-phosphate y*
E140	*Chlorophylls and chlorophyllins*		
E150a	*Plain caramel*	E153	*Vegetable carbon*
E160a	*Carotenes*	E160b	*Annatto; Bixin; Norbixin*
E160c	*Paprika extract; Capsanthian; Capsorubin*		
E160d	*Lycopene*	E160e	*Beta-apo-8'-carotenal (C30)*
E161b	*Lutein*	E161g	*Canthaxanthin*
E162	*Beetroot Red; Betanin*	E163	*Anthocyanins*
E170	*Calcium carbonate*	E171	*Titanium dioxide*
E172	*Iron oxides and hydroxides*	E200	*Sorbic acid*
E220	*Sulphur dioxide*	E221	*Sodium sulphite*
E222	*Sodium hydrogen sulphite*	E223	*Sodium metabisulphite*
E224	*Potassium metabisulphite*	E226	*Calcium sulphite*
E227	*Calcium hydrogen sulphite*	E228	*Potassium hydrogen sulphite*
E249	*Potassium nitrite*	E250	*Sodium nitrite*
E251	*Sodium nitrate*	E252	*Potassium nitrate*
E280	*Propionic acid*	E281	*Sodium propionate*
E282	*Calcium propionate*	E283	*Potassium propionate*
E284	*Boric acid*	E1105	*Lysozyme*

E300	Ascorbic acid	E301	Sodium ascorbate
E302	Calcium ascorbate	E322	Lecithins
E426	Soybean hemicellulose	E440	Pectins

E470a Sodium, potassium and calcium salts of fatty acids

E470b Magnesium salts of fatty acids

E471 Mono- and diglycerides of fatty acids

E472a Acetic acid esters of mono- and diglycerides of fatty acids

E472b Lactic acid esters of mono- and diglycerides of fatty acids

E472c Citric acid esters of mono- and diglycerides of fatty acids

E472d Tartaric acid esters of mono- and diglycerides of fatty acids

E473	Sucrose esters of fatty acids	E474	Sucroglycerides
E1103	Invertase	E260	Acetic acid
E261	Potassium acetate	E262	Sodium acetate
E263	Calcium acetate	E270	Lactic acid
E290	Carbon dioxide	E296	Malic acid
E297	Fumaric acid	E325	Sodium lactate
E326	Potassium lactate	E327	Calcium lactate
E330	Citric acid	E331	Sodium citrates
E332	Potassium citrates	E333	Calcium citrates
E334	Tartaric acid	E335	Sodium tartrates
E336	Potassium tartrates	E337	Sodium potassium tartrate
E341	Calcium phosphates	E422	Glycerol
E450	Diphosphates	E451	Triphosphates
E452	Polyphosphates	E459	Beta-cyclodextrin
E500	Sodium carbonates	E507	Hydrochloric acid
E508	Potassium chloride	E509	Calcium chloride
E511	Magnesium chloride	E551	Silicon dioxide
E570	Fatty acids	E574	Gluconic acid
E620	Glutamic acid	E621	Monosodium glutamate
E634	Calcium 5'-ribonucleotides	E635	Disodium 5'-ribonucleotides
E640	Glycine and its sodium salt	E914	Oxidised polyethylene wax
E920	L-Cysteine	E938	Argon
E939	Helium	E941	Nitrogen
E948	Oxygen	E949	Hydrogen
E1200	Polydextrose		

My top ten favourite Es

1 – E300 (Vitamin C). Unlike those of the vast majority of mammals and plants, the human body cannot synthesize this vitamin, yet it's essential for life. Without it, we can't create enough collagen (the connective tissue in our bodies) and we quickly develop scurvy and effectively then rot and fall apart. Vitamin C is also a powerful antioxidant, an essential ingredient in the process whereby our bodies create the important biochemicals we need to function*. No vitamin C, no human race.

2 – E220 (Sulphur dioxide). This is going to sound a little selfish, but bear with me. Sulphur dioxide is to blame for more problems than any other E. It's pretty much the only E with any clearly defined and really sizeable intolerance, with around 4% of asthmatics having their condition aggravated by it (and the risk is doubled in steroid-dependent asthmatics). If there's a bad boy in the E team, it's SO_2. But why do I love it so? Not because I have anything against asthmatics, but because it is also responsible for more pleasure than any other E. It's the preservative that's found in almost every bottle of wine on the planet, and has been present in most bottles since Roman times. It's why almost every bottle of wine label reads 'Contains sulphites'. Without SO_2, wine generally has a strong tang of rotten apples mixed with a splash of rotten cabbage (I know this because I've tasted wine without it). Five hundred years ago, Dutch and English wine traders burned sulphur candles inside barrels before filling them. Although SO_2 causes problems, it's a classic case of an E whose benefits outweigh the risks, and it's so important as an antioxidant, preservative and bleaching agent that it's permitted for use in organic foods too. EU regulations mean that if it's in food it must be highlighted on the label, so if you know you're intolerant you can avoid it.

3 – CSB Actually, it's not just an E, but a cocktail of them. It's the acronym for Corn Soy Blend, a food that's handed out by the World Food Programme as emergency food aid, and which has saved millions of lives across the world. It's about 70% cornmeal and 27% soy flour and soybean oil, together with lots of E number additives in a mineral and vitamin antioxidant premix. It contains riboflavin (E101), vitamin C (E300), vitamin E (E306/7/8/9) and various less glamorous Es to stabilize,

---

* Technically, it's an enzyme cofactor for biosynthesis, acting as an electron donator for several different enzymes.

preserve and process the flours. It provides a huge dose of essential nutrients that are particularly difficult for people to find in refugee and disaster situations. I ate it when I spent some time in refugee camps in Ethiopia and Northern Uganda, and although it's very bland it's easy to cook (just add water and it puffs up into a thick mash) and it saves lives. Thank God it exists.

4 – E500 (ii) (Sodium bicarbonate). If this wasn't in our world, cakes wouldn't rise.

5 – E322 (Lecithin). It's the emulsifier that keeps cocoa and cocoa butter in chocolate bars from separating. Call me low-brow if you like, but I enjoy milk chocolate, so all hail E322. It can be entirely metabolized in the body and it's non-toxic at anything but absurd levels of consumption.

6 – E120 (Cochineal). This is made from the casings of the cochineal scale insect (see entry on page 76). I've had a large bag of the unprocessed bugs sitting on my desk for the past two years, and I feel that they have become my friends. If you grind just one or two of these tiny bugs using a mortar and pestle, you can turn a large volume of water into a livid pink. There's no medical or nutritional reason for liking them – they're just fun.

7 – E160a (ii) (Beta carotene). I've always secretly harboured a childish desire to eat so many carrots that I experienced carotenodermia, a harmless pigmentation condition whereby your skin turns orange. E160a (ii) is sold as a nutritional supplement, although there has been an association between high doses of these supplements and lung cancer in smokers.

8 – E401 (Sodium alginate). Used for making apple caviar. Alginate is capable of absorbing 200–300 times its own weight of water, and it can be used to form a viscous gum. When you drop a solution of this (say, with an apple liquor) into a solution containing E509 (calcium chloride), you can create little caviar-like balls. This technique is know as spherification and it's a bit of molecular gastronomy flippancy, but it's quite good fun. On a more boring level, it's also used in indigestion tablets and dehydrated slimming aids to help them absorb more water.

9 – E407 (Carrageenan). It's in Ben & Jerry's Cherry Garcia ice cream. Made from seaweed, this E has been associated with a range of medical problems at high levels of consumption, but is subject to very tight regulations in the food trade to ensure that usage stays at acceptable levels. Remove it at your peril.

10 – E412 (Guar gum). A pretty simple substance, made from guar bean seeds, but with a range of rather good side effects, preventing constipation, Crohn's disease, IBS and colitis, helping diabetics slow the absorption of sugar, helping the intestines to remove toxins from the system and all manner of other good stuff.

The bad,
the misunderstood
and the misguided

Bad Es

Like all foods, E numbers are toxic at a high enough dose, but EU law heavily regulates all Es, and it is important to remember that *everything* including water is toxic at a high enough concentration. Nonetheless there are several very controversial Es that have been in the news and which beg extra attention, and there will always be people allergic to any food. Although 7% of the UK *think* that they are intolerant to food additives only around 0.01–0.23 actually are, but if you have specific allergies you should avoid the substances identified as their cause. For instance, if you are allergic to benzoic acid and benzoates (E210–215), you'll also need to avoid cranberries, which are naturally stacked with it. If you think you are allergic to MSG, you will also need to avoid most cheese, tomatoes, hams, mushrooms, peas, nuts, chicken, beef, eggs and pork.

The most-often cited intolerance to additives concerns sulphites, and benzoate preservatives and synthetic food colours, although the context is interesting: while eight foods account for 90% of food allergies in the developed world, none of them are additives. The first additive comes in at no.12.

Here are the leading causes of food allergies and intolerances in order of importance:

1. Peanuts
2. Tree nuts, such as pecans, walnuts
3. Fish
4. Shellfish
5. Eggs
6. Milk
7. Soya
8. Wheat
9. Mustard
10. Celery
11. Sesame seeds
12. Sulphur dioxide (E220)

Sulphur dioxide
Practically all wine is made with sulphur dioxide (E220), and it has been for thousands of years. When you read 'Contains sulphites' on the label, that's what it's telling you. The statistics are pretty clear: sulphites aggravate asthma in around 4% of sufferers and the reaction can be severe. The amount used in wine has been lowered by regulations, but without it most wine tastes foul, so the best advice if you are asthmatic is to avoid wine altogether unless you can find one of the handful of sulphite-free wines.

The Southampton Six colours
In September 2007, a decent, well-designed FSA-funded study* by researchers at Southampton University showed that a mixture of six artificial colours, together with sodium benzoate (E211) could increase hyperactivity in children. The colours were: sunset yellow (E110), quinoline yellow (E104), carmoisine (E122), allura red (E129), tartrazine (E102) and ponceau 4R (E124). Two years later the Authority introduced a voluntary phasing-out of these colours (although not a ban).

So do all these colours really cause hyperactivity? Well, it's not quite as

* Food additives and hyperactive behaviour in 3-year-old and 8/9-year-old children in the community: a randomized, double-blinded, placebo controlled trial. *The Lancet*, 370, 1560–1567.

simple as that – in fact this study is a little frustrating as it only proves that this specific *mixture* of six colours, together with sodium benzoate, could cause hyperactivity (as the EFSA pointed out when they analysed the data. They also questioned the significance of the effects and mentioned 'the small changes in attention and activity observed'*). I can understand if you think that's splitting hairs, but blaming seven substances for a problem begs the question 'Was it caused by one, some, or all of the substances, and what was the actual root cause?' That information could have been extremely useful, especially now that manufacturers may look to other colours at higher concentrations or start using natural colourings that may sound better, but have lower standards of toxicity testing. The FSA is absolutely right to advise that 'if your child shows signs of hyperactivity or Attention Deficit Hyperactivity Disorder, you should try to avoid giving your child [these six] artificial colours.'**

Aspartame E951

This powerful artificial sweetener is one of the most thoroughly tested food additives in the world*** and is used in everything from Coca-Cola (which you may well dislike, but millions enjoy) to ice cream. It is used as a replacement for sugar in low-calorie or diet products so that consumers can lower their calorie intake. It does have one small drawback: you may have seen on the ingredients list that it contains phenylalanine, which on one hand is an essential nutrient that our bodies can't synthesize and so must get from food, but on the other hand causes problems to phenylketonuria sufferers (a genetic disease affecting 1 in 15,000 people – i.e. 4,000 or so in the UK) who *might* benefit from trying to control the amount they consume just as a diabetic must control their sugar intake.

But aspartame has been the subject of some very odd controversies since it was first approved in 1974 in the USA. In 1999 a (quite possibly fictitious) character called 'Nancy Markle' claimed that aspartame was responsible for multiple sclerosis, systematic lupus, birth defects, methanol toxicity and dangerous formaldehyde levels in the body. This is all untrue***, but the information was spread around the world by chain emails and became

---

* http://www.efsa.europa.eu/EFSA/efsa_locale-1178620753812_1178694645855.htm
** http://www.eatwell.gov.uk/healthissues/foodintolerance/foodintolerancetypes/foodadditiv/hype/additivesbehaviour/
*** http://www.ctahr.hawaii.edu/oc/freepubs/pdf/FST-3.pdf

part of common paranoia about aspartame. 'Nancy Markle' became a test case for determining the credibility of information sources on the Media Awareness Network****.

A whole series of murky events did take place in connection to the long, drawn-out approval process in the USA and subsequent investigations into how it was handled, and there have been various scares about aspartame and brain tumours, epilepsy and neurological problems, but they have since been extensively researched without any causal link made*****. Importantly, we get a much higher intake of the component parts of aspartame (aspartic acid, phenylalanine, aspartic acid and methanol) from a normal diet than from even a high consumption of food or drink using it as an additive. Most food scientists laugh at the dangers of aspartame in colas in comparison to the caffeine (a psychoactive stimulant that can cause sleep and anxiety disorders, but which has no E number).

Diphosphates (E450)

While there's nothing wrong with diphosphates in nutritional terms, they can be used to make meat retain water so that it appears to be bulkier. You could either read this as a way to con the public to pay for water, thinking it's meat, or it could be a useful way to make meat more succulent. Perhaps a little of both.

Sodium nitrate (E251) and potassium nitrate (E252)

Nitrates, together with nitrites are preservatives used in cured meats (especially bacon) and they also help keep the colour red or pink rather than greyish (this process has been used for hundreds, if not thousands of years and the substances used to be known as saltpetre, but the E tag has now been given to it). But bacon-eaters across the world were either scared or appalled in 2009 when the World Cancer Research Fund said there was convincing evidence that red (their definition of red meat includes beef, pork, lamb and goat) and processed meat are causes of bowel cancer. This is no small claim, seeing as around 16,000 people die of bowel cancer every year.

Seems pretty clear cut. But hang on. The WCRF adds to that list 'any meat that has been preserved by curing, salting or smoking' as well as 'hot

---

**** http://www.media-awareness.ca/english/resources/educational/teaching_backgrounders/internet/decon_web_pages.cfm
*****http://ec.europa.eu/food/fs/sc/scf/out155_en.pdf

dogs, ham, bacon and some sausages and burgers'. That's a large chunk of an omnivore's food pool, and altering that as a major source of nutrition takes a massive lifestyle and economic change. As someone on the *Guardian* blog wrote 'They'll take my salami and ham out of my cold, dead hands'. Also the WCRF don't give much detail about how much you're cutting your risk of bowel cancer, but do state that there are lots of other ways of cutting your risk, too. Cancer Research UK are a little more guarded, saying that 'there is reasonably consistent evidence that eating a lot of red meat…particularly processed meat, could increase your risk of bowel cancer.' Helpfully they do say that chicken and turkey probably don't increase your risk of bowel cancer. Incidentally, I took a peek at the ingredients for Duchy Originals Organic Dry Cure Streaky Bacon and was a little surprised to find sodium nitrate E251 there (not listed with its E number, naturally – just its name; a technique which I always find a little cheeky).

I am an avowed fan of cured meats so I asked Sarah Maines, (a molecular biologist at the Medical Research Council who specializes in the links between diet and cancer), and she said there was, indeed, a small increased risk from preservatives. Nitrates and nitrites form nitrosamines during very high-temperature cooking and these are *potentially* carcinogenic, although she was at pains to add that the concentrations in bacon are tiny, at 10–20 parts per billion, and far, far smaller than the levels that were found to cause cancer. The trouble is that this happens during the Maillard reaction, the very process that every chef holds dear for its addition of magical flavours when meat is seared or vegetables are fried in hot fat. Sarah added that when potatoes are fried at high temperatures, a compound called asparagine reacts with sugars to form acrylamides – another carcinogen. Oh my God – what's left to eat? The word 'carcinogen' scares the bejesus out of me. But Sarah explained that it's not at all clear whether or not the level of acrylamides in fried food could give you cancer – and there are carcinogens in lots of natural foods in varying doses anyway (see page 33).

So can we say that nitrates and nitrites are *probably* bad for you? Well, no, not necessarily. Sarah, who incidentally was heavily pregnant when I interviewed her, spoke with great enthusiasm about nitrates and nitrites. 'You know what? I wouldn't touch that bacon *without* the nitrates in it. It's healthier as it is. What you've got to remember', she said, 'is that without these preservatives you are much more likely to get pathogens in the meat, such as *Clostridium botulinum* and those are much bigger problems.' A more manipulative writer might remind you that a single teaspoon of botulism toxin could kill the entire population of the UK, but I wouldn't do a thing like that.

So the benefits from having preservatives in your meat are greater than the risks if you don't have them. And, of course, if you eat fresh fish or poultry instead, you are just shifting the risk on to food sources that are generally safe, but also renowned for *salmonella, campylobacter* (30,000 cases formally notified, translating into an estimated half a million annual cases of UK food poisoning) and *Clostridium perfringens*.

Aaaargh! Do we need to stop eating everything that brings us joy? No. Sarah suggests we put the risk into context with the other risks we experience on a daily basis and instead try to spread our diet between as many different foods as we can and concentrate on other issues: stop smoking, avoid getting burnt in the sun, cut down on alcohol, get more exercise, eat well, cook fresh food when you can, and enjoy life.

MAP – Modified Atmospheric Packaging

The use of Es sometimes has tangential negative effects and MAP may be one of those. It's the use of atmospheric gases to package foods. If you take one of those bags of salad that looks like a little pillow, and it says on the side 'Packaged in a protective atmosphere'. That doesn't mean the factory was nice and clean – it means that the bag is full of carbon dioxide or nitrogen, with only a very little oxygen. Open it quickly and put a lit match in it and it will go out instantly. Now I know it sounds weird and science-y to pump food with nitrogen, but this stuff really isn't odd – it's all around us anyway – making up 78% of the air we breathe. They put it in mainly to pump *out* the bulk of the oxygen so that the food 'goes to sleep' yet 'breathes' very slowly so it doesn't wilt and discolour. This keeps it fresh and crisp in the bag and gives it a longer shelf-life.*

However, it also means, as Felicity Lawrence describes so well in her book *Not on the Label*, that it looks a bit healthier than it is – the nutrient levels drop in the MAP-bagged salad just as quickly as the unbagged salad, but the former still looks like it's fresh and healthy. You could see this as a con, or you could say that you just want crispy salad. I just hate bagged salads for cost and packaging reasons, myself.

---

* http://www.modifiedatmospherepackaging.net

MSG

No self-respecting book on Es could be complete without a good old poke at monosodium glutamate (E621); the world's most widely used flavour-enhancer and the world's most demonized food additive. There are whole web sites and armies of nutritionists who blame it for everything from high blood pressure, asthmatic symptoms, and sleep disturbance to digestive problems. However, there is no robust clinical evidence to prove that there's much wrong with MSG, (although as a salt it adds slightly to your sodium intake), and lots of reliable evidence to prove that it's very safe indeed. I know that this may run counter to everything you've heard about food additives (even I can't rid myself of an irrational fear of the stuff), and it's true that there are some unpleasant processed foods that contain it, but it's extremely unlikely that MSG is bad for you. In fact, glutamate is very good indeed – so good that our bodies wouldn't be able to function without it. Our bodies produce 50g of glutamate every day independently of the food we eat and it's an amino acid found in all living cells. Glutamate occurs entirely naturally in many foods and Parmesan contains more glutamate than you could find in any processed food (and by the way, it's *not* the substance that makes cheap Chinese food thick and gloopy – that's just rice flour or cornflour).

MSG is usually made by fermenting sugar beet or molasses, and the glutamate was first isolated in 1908 by Kikunae Ikeda, a Japanese scientist who wondered why his wife's dashi stock tasted so good. It's used as an additive to help the flavour of many soups, sauces, sausages, instant noodle packs and lots of snacks and also has its own distinct taste – savoury or *umami*, also known as the fifth taste alongside salty, sweet, bitter and sour. The difference between monosodium glutamate and naturally-occurring free glutamate is simply the extra sodium that keeps the glutamate in a stable, usable powder, and which dissolves away when we eat it*. And don't go thinking that sodium is a necessarily a bad thing either – it's also an essential element for all animal life.

* A 2006 review of the last 40 years of research into MSG and CRS concludes that 'clinical trials have failed to identify a consistent relationship between the consumption of MSG and the constellation of symptoms that comprise the syndrome. Furthermore, MSG has been described as a trigger for asthma and migraine headache exacerbations, but there are no consistent data to support this relationship. Although there have been reports of an MSG-sensitive subset of the population, this has not been demonstrated in placebo-controlled trials.'
Reconsidering the effects of monosodium glutamate: A literature review, Matthew Freeman, CNP, *Journal of the American Academy of Nurse Practitioners*

So why are we so afraid of MSG? It all seems to have started in 1969 with an article in *Science* journal linking MSG and *Chinese Restaurant Syndrome*. This sparked enormous interest as well as a widespread fear of MSG, and precipitated an avalanche of subsequent studies. The trouble is that extensive placebo-controlled double-blind clinical studies have failed to connect CRS symptoms with MSG intake, even at very high doses*. But MSG and Chinese food have never managed to shake off the stench of bad nutrition, despite the fact that Italian food contains far more glutamate than Chinese (it's found especially in Parmesan cheese, tomatoes, mushrooms and in huge amounts in some seaweeds such as konbu). Ever wondered why your pasta is transformed when you grate a handful of Parmesan cheese over it? Yup: you are scattering a large dose of glutamate over your food. For the E numbers TV series we gathered together a group of people who believed that they had a bad sensitivity to MSG. We fed them a Chinese meal extremely low in natural glutamate and an Italian meal high in natural glutamate. Half of the Chinese meal consumers reported severe CRS symptoms, as did one of the Italian meal consumers. Yet neither meal contained any MSG.

This is not to say that CRS symptoms are phantoms or that sufferers are deluded – they may well be experiencing these symptoms, it's just extremely unlikely to be MSG that's causing them. In the unlikely event that they really are sensitive to glutamate in food, they should also avoid most hard cheeses, soy sauce, walnuts, peas, mushrooms, tomatoes, sweetcorn and chicken. Even breast milk has 11 times as much glutamate as cows' milk. No one, annoyingly, has worked out the real cause of CRS.

Of course, just because the MSG is safe, it doesn't mean the food it's in is nice or healthy. There are plenty of grim soups and instant noodle pots containing MSG that I personally think are disgusting, and if you eat too much fatty, salty or sugary food, you are likely to cause yourself problems whatever else is in it. There *could* be a twist if you like seeing the conspiracy theory in these kinds of things: that MSG tastes so good that we are drawn to eating lots of processed foods that contain it, and as these foods may contain other things that are bad for you, we are led into a nutritional trap. It's a bit far-fetched, but it's a theory.

---

* In *On Food and Cooking*, Harold McGee says that '[after many studies], toxicologists have concluded that MSG is a harmless ingredient for most people, even in large amounts.'
Other studies: Geha RS, Beiser A, Ren C, et al. (April 2000). "Review of alleged reaction to monosodium glutamate and outcome of a multicenter double-blind placebo-controlled study". J. Nutr. 130 (4S Suppl): 1058S–62S. PMID 10736382.

Why are we afraid of Es?

In 1984, European food labelling regulations made food manufacturers declare the additives in their food by their E numbers and that same year Maurice Hanssen published a groundbreaking book called *E for Additives* that revealed what these Es meant. The public was shocked at what they learned and the book became an award-winning bestseller. It's a great, remarkably restrained book, but 26 years later, after extensive research and regulation, some media nutritionists inspired by the book seem to ignore the facts and get their science very, very wrong indeed. Yet because they are excellent at promoting themselves, they get on TV. I've been wondering why we listen to them.

UK consumer expenditure on food, drink and catering was £173 billion in 2008, and there are currently 3.1 million people working in the UK food chain. The UK is the world's eighth largest exporter of food and drink. The industry is vast. The potential for conspiracy, political shenanigans and sheer fight for economic advantage means that there will always be scandal and malpractice somewhere. It makes sense to mistrust these people on some level, but although the heavily regulated Es system is not the most important place to focus our fears on, I can understand why we do. I should add that the next two paragraphs are pure, unadulterated speculation.

Firstly, we have an inbuilt dislike of the idea of finding science and chemistry in our food – we like to think of food and cooking as an art rather than a science. We find science complex and scary and out of our control, and hence there seems to be ample opportunity for scientists, government and industry to conspire against us. The E system sounds cold, science-ey and remote from our experience for those of us who like buying real, tactile, good-looking food in markets and supermarkets. Giving an ingredient a code and a letter really is a masterpiece of bad marketing, and tying it to substances with names we can barely pronounce let alone understand just makes us suspicious.

Secondly, it serves nutritionists, reporters and the huge nutritional supplements industry well to see the food industry as suspicious and conspiratorial as it gives them a target to aim their ire at. I'm not saying that they knowingly lie about additives (in fact I'm sure they believe what they are saying), and they may well provide other useful advice to their clients, but without a pariah like Es to suggest avoiding, these people's roles are weakened.

Thirdly, we are simply nervous of all food – perhaps part of our hard-wired evolutionary attitude that helps us to avoid being poisoned, or perhaps because we are all hypochondriacs. Either way, there's a huge gap between perceived allergies and intolerances of food and the reality (7% of us believe we have an allergy or intolerance to food additives as opposed to the 0.01–0.23% who actually do).

Fourthly, there have been lots of anti-E hoaxes and disinformation about Es, and even when they are disproved, our fear continues. The more highly successful hoaxes include the 1999 'Nancy Markle'/aspartame/MS/ birth defects scare (see page 47) and the Villejuif List, a hoax claiming to be from a Parisian hospital. It listed a number of perfectly safe food additives including citric acid and alleged that they were carcinogenic. It sounds funny now, but it brought on mass panic across Europe in the 1970s and continued to do so until at least 1984, causing unquantifiable anxiety and nutritional harm after schools, hospitals and social organizations spread the information. Half the housewives of France were estimated to have read it*. People react dramatically and easily to food scares but it takes enormous time and effort to put the facts right and reassure them.

Dr Gillian McKeith – oops sorry, it's just Gillian McKeith in her product advertisements now – got several TV series on Channel 4 and often levelled the guns of her formidable nutritional knowledge at food additives. Just to show how even a nutritional expert can sometimes get the source wrong, in Gillian McKeith's seminal text on nutrition *You Are What You Eat* ('Slimmer, healthier and happier… that's my promise to you') she makes some very interesting statements. She says 'Steer clear of foods made with artificial colours. Watch out for… Beetroot Red (E162)', but then four sentences later that 'red pigments obtained from beets… are OK'. Hang on… yes, you guessed it, E162 Beetroot Red is obtained from… beets. She says that 'citric acid and ascorbic acid… are natural antioxidants added to a number of foods' (when citric and ascorbic acids are added to foods they are almost always chemically synthesized, and the fact that they are synthetic rather than natural makes no difference whatsoever), that 'Sodium is just another name for salt' (it's not), that 'transfatty acid is another name for hydrogenated fat' (it's not), and that artificial colours damage your immune system and speed up ageing (not sure how she worked that one out). She also offers bizarre advice, such as eating chlorophyll to purify your blood (an extremely odd concept). I'm sure Gillian isn't writing this for any bad reasons, but it just doesn't add up.

She says that 'additives place a huge stress on your body because your body has to work harder to deal with them, with the result that energy and valuable nutrients are spent when they could be used more profitably, for example in boosting the immune system.' This has no basis in medical understanding of the metabolic process. Our body just recognizes the molecules, not where they have come from. It is like people thinking that olive oil is lower in calories because it is 'healthy', or that unrefined sugar is better than white sugar – the body just sees the sucrose molecule and uses the relevant enzymes to digest it, the same with those based on fat, or starch, etc., etc. Monoglycerides of fatty acids sound really chemical, but they are just fats, and our bodies digest them like any other fat.

Many good-hearted people and organizations have aimed their guns at the additives industry, and their advice sometimes takes on the mantle of expertise, whether it deserves it or not. In *E for Additives*, the seminal book on Es, one organization's dietary advice is quoted again and again as proof that there's something deeply wrong with Es, the Hyperactive Children's Support Group. Now, this may indeed be an important source of help for people whose children show signs of hyperactivity, but a little investigation seems to point to a strange attitude to scientific knowledge at its heart.

Apparently, 'The brain consists of lipids – that is, fats – that the body cannot manufacture and can only obtain through the food we eat.' Well, there are indeed lipids in the brain, but a lipid-only brain would be a very floppy thing indeed without the other stuff that holds it all together. What about all those nucleic acids, sugars and proteins (ironically, one of the most important proteins is glutamic acid, a crucial neurotransmitter, but which is also eaten in additive form as MSG, a substance the HACSG dislikes)?

Then, when you take a look at the organization's work, things get a little murkier. The HACSG discusses how its groundbreaking research into fatty acid deficiencies as a factor in ADHD was published in *Medical Hypotheses*, 7(5), 1981. This all sounds very upright and clinical, doesn't it? Except that when you investigate *Medical Hypotheses*, you find that it's actually a publication dedicated to radical and non-mainstream ideas, and it specifically *isn't* a peer-review journal, ensuring that research published in it is never publicly taken to task. Which is a good job really, seeing as

* http://www.jstor.org/pss/2749354

Medical Hypotheses has published articles by AIDS denialists, by authors who suggested the term 'mongoloid' was appropriate for people with Down's Syndrome (partly because they shared characteristics with Asians, including eating foods containing MSG), and by writers presenting masturbation as a treatment for nasal congestion. The HACSG may well have a useful role to play but it chooses interesting ways to make itself heard.

The spread of nutritionism as a non-academic, casual, psychobabble-based and anecdotal-evidence reliant profession worries me enormously. Anyone can call themselves a nutritionist and even when they do have qualifications, some of those qualifications seem strangely easy to come by. These people sometimes feed on fear, and earn their money from it, advising people to avoid E numbers and bemoaning MSG, while recommending bizarre supplements like horny goat weed complex. Many are, of course, promoting their range of diet books, packs of branded seeds and nutritional supplements as part of the $50-billion worldwide food supplement pill industry.

But when it comes down to it, the E number system is a textbook disaster of bad marketing. It must have seemed like such as good idea to the EU food scientists at the time: give the public lots of information and they can make choices based on what's in their food and feel more confident that we're looking after their safety. 'I know, we'll put an E in front so they know it's the European food safety guys they have to thank, and then give them the code number so they can look up the preservative. They'll love us for this.'

I bet they never imagined that their system would become so universally hated. And now we think that all additives are essentially the same thing so if one additive gets a bad reputation, they all do.

So everyone's scared of all of them. And I'll make an admission here: in a strange way I am still afraid of E numbers, too. Despite everything I know and all I've learnt, the fear that's been instilled in me from my 42 years of reading, watching and listening to so many people I respect whipping up this heady mix of fear, guilt and confusion has meant that the idea of them still has a residual discomforting sense that they are wrong. Fear and disinformation have a mighty power.

Don't be afraid. Understand.

Let's get all this in context. There are many delicious, artisan-produced, organic and nutritious foods that contain E numbers and without which life would be infinitely less enjoyable (my favourites include cereals, wine, fine hams, cheese, olives, cakes and fruit juices). There are also lots of grim-tasting and nutritionally bereft pizzas, nuggets and cakes that contain Es. But it's not Es that make foods rubbish – it's rubbish food producers, bad cooks, poverty and lack of knowledge.

There are some Es that a small amount of people may be intolerant of, although they pale into insignificance beside the vast range of natural foods that can cause severe allergic reactions or that naturally contain toxins or carcinogens. Es may help the food industry make more money, and can be used to turn slop into something that looks attractive to eat, but there's a positive side: they give us vitamin- and mineral-enrichment, disease-preventing foods, low-sugar, low-fat and low-salt foods, convenient, flavoursome and attractive foods as well as cheap, long-lasting food that people (perhaps not you) enjoy. And many of them occur naturally in our bodies and in foods we already eat.

So why have I bothered to write this book? Really, what's so wrong with people worrying about the Es in their food? If they don't like the idea of eating additives and are prepared just to listen to one side of the argument, what's the problem? And, in any case, surely an industry we spend £173 billion on every year can stand up for itself?

The problem is that it's a huge and damaging distraction from the real disasters unfolding in Britain: the 3 million people suffering from, or at risk of, malnutrition, the 12 million cases of infectious intestinal disease every year, bad nutrition caused by a paucity of food education, food poisoning from bad preparation and storage of fresh food, premature death from eating disorders like anorexia, high-fat and high-sugar diets leading to obesity and related diseases, high-salt diets increasing stroke and heart disease.

So, while many self-appointed nutritionists and the media love to hate Es, most clinical healthcare professionals, microbiologists and cancer specialists tend to think there are much more important food and nutrition issues to tackle.

Dr Jonty Heaversedge runs a busy urban GP surgery caring for 15,000 patients in a deprived inner-city London borough. He'd never say this, but if there's a front line of medical care, he's on it. Here's his view on E number paranoia:

'The risk of focusing on E numbers is that we distract ourselves from the real issues facing us, as individuals, as a nation and as a rapidly developing world. Millions of people are dying every year from the complications of diabetes, heart disease and stroke – and millions more are made miserable through living with chronic ill health. The culprits are not E numbers, but the fat, sugar and salt in our diet. If everyone in the UK could reduce their salt intake to just 3 grams a day it is estimated we could prevent 50,000 strokes a year. And this is just a drop in the ocean when you compare it to the statistics for diabetes. There are over 250 million people in the world whose lives are being shortened by this disease, and this number is likely to rise to 438 million in the next 20 years – yet we focus our worries on a well regulated system for identifying the additives manufacturers can put in the food? Talk about fiddling while Rome burns! No one is suggesting we ignore the consequences of anything we ingest but lets just try and keep things in perspective.'

Dr Lisa Ackerley (Professor of Environmental Health at Salford University) is particularly concerned about vital issues that are all but they drowned out by the noise of E hysteria: 'One little-discussed issue is that of sick pay for food handlers who are ill with infectious diseases. Statutory sick pay doesn't kick in until 3 normal working days after someone is off sick. So if you are on a minimum wage and money is tight (often the case for food industry workers) and if your employer doesn't pay sick pay (again often the case) then you would get no pay for 3 days and then only a meagre amount when you do become eligible. Who is going to admit to having diarrhoea or sickness in these circumstances when it could make them behind with the rent or mortgage? Sick staff can easily spread diseases such as salmonella or norovirus, so we've got to have a system that pays such key workers to stay away from work when they are infectious. The joke is that many of them will be better in three days – just when they would be eligible for some pay!'

The food industry is unlikely to jump to solve these problems – it does very nicely out of fatty, sugary and salty foods, thanks very much, and will do so until our buying habits change. And in any case, we are rightly far too wary as consumers to trust a £173 billion industry to do the right thing – there's too much cash at stake. The additives backlash has already made food manufacturers scared of admitting what they put in their food, so they pick and choose whichever sounds best between an additive's name or number to put on labels where there is a public concern. I don't like paranoia, but less information can't be a good thing.

The grand conspiracy theories about the government-science-food-business complex poisoning us with E numbers achieve three negative things: 1. It encourages consumers to abrogate responsibility for their health by implying that the responsibility for bad nutrition is out of their hands. 2. It increases public paranoia and thereby lays the foundations for another industry to counter the conspiracy. 3. That industry is the multi-billion pound nutritionist and nutritional supplements industry that provides often desperate and expensive solutions based on flimsy evidence (see pages 54–57).

Of course, the truth is that most consumers and politicians don't want to tackle the big nutritional problems facing our country because they are irritatingly difficult to solve and take inspiration, self-discipline, education, investment and effort. It's so much easier to blame something faceless, that we perceive there's little we can do about. Something like E numbers.

While researching this book I've come across so many people who seem to have ceded personal responsibility for their health by blaming a faceless conspiracy of Es without showing any understanding of them. These people are often angrily critical of Es, but only in vague holistic-nutrition terms: they're not sure exactly why, but they are sure they ought to hate

Es. That's what all the chefs and nutritionists say on the telly and in the papers, isn't it?

When I asked one very prominent food scientist if additives are really necessary she said that 'additives are generally quite expensive ingredients so manufacturers can't afford to add them unless they are needed, and then at the minimum level to get the desired effect.

'If they wanted to make cheap food they'd want to add more air and water, as these are the cheap ingredients! I don't like the cheap food that is produced, but if this is removed, what about the people currently on the poverty line? Education is the thing, as it is possible to eat healthily and cheaply, but you have to do some work yourself, as a consumer, not sit on your arse and try to blame the food manufacturers!'

Cheap food

Which brings us to the thorny issue of cheap food, whether enabled by additives or not. I know that the idea of food being cheap makes many people spit fire, although I suspect that those that hate it are mainly the people who can afford expensive food as opposed to the millions of people who are malnourished or at risk of malnourishment and who spend a disproportionate amount of their income on food already. Of course, you can eat cheaply and marvelously well on unprocessed vegetables and cheaper cuts of meat, but we must acknowledge that to do so requires knowledge, aptitude and the will and time to cook, which many people are sadly lacking. Education and inspiration seem to be the keys to a healthier diet, yet these are notoriously hard to come by.

There's nothing wrong with food being inexpensive, although there's a lot wrong with a lot of cheap food. I should know: I ate enough of both in the Seventies… and the Eighties… and much of the Nineties, now I think about it. Cheap, nasty pseudo-burgers and marge as a kid, then massive curries I made out of bacon off-cuts and root veg as a student, and then some delicious frugal feasts made on a budget as I struggled under the weight of massive student debts once I'd landed in the real world.

But lest we be tempted to start reiterating the dull clichés of the food world about people's obsession with the price of food rather than the quality, lets get some perspective: the poorest fifth of people in Britain spend around one-third of their income on food. That's a huge proportion, and any changes in the price of food can cause real hardship. However much you might love your artisan bread, a cheap long-life sliced loaf is important to many people because it's simply all they can afford.

There's a lot of cheap rubbish food around, some of it enabled by various E numbers and some of it totally additive-free. I've just eaten a small range of E-packed crap for my lunch as research: frozen loaves of flat bread masquerading as pizzas, with flavour-free but salt-heavy toppings on them (and lots of Es). Then I taste-tested a can of Heinz Big Soup that was a marvel of un-additive-ness. Not a preservative, flavour enhancer, colour or emulsifier in sight. And gruesome it was: not a flavour in sight either. I was practically craving MSG and I had to stop eating it halfway through to fry a little garlic and add Parmesan, salt, chilli and cumin to make it edible.

Then there's the worst food I've ever tried (and just so you understand my frame of reference, I've eaten *igunak* (rotten walrus) and radioactive borscht): canned meatloaf. This solid, pinky-orangey block of reformed, mechanically recovered meat that sits in front of my keyboard looks and smells oddly similar to my body fat (see page 35).

But while these products are cheap and not particularly nice, it still feels like snobbery to berate people for buying them. If people like these, or they can't afford better, what's to be done? Take them off the shelves? Who am I to say that someone shouldn't eat something they want to eat? This stuff is cheap, and it's not for me, but really, if that's your thing, or it suits your lifestyle or your budget to get a can of meat that doesn't rot, and which you can slice and eat in a flash for a big hit of calories, and you enjoy the fat and the salt, who am I to stop you?

I can't stand TV presenters who lift these products up in front of a camera and poke fun at the people who buy them but don't offer any solution or alternative. They never seem to meet people who are buying canned meat loaf to ask why they like it, and this smacks of smugness and snobbery. I asked several buyers in my local shops, and and there was a genuine, if mild, enthusiasm amongst the buyers. Most people simply said that it was cheap and they liked eating it. One very funny elderly lady looked at me and frowned: 'I've eaten this ever since I was a child. It's cheap, and it's nice.' You can't argue with that, and I didn't even bother to offer an alternative for fear of being slapped.

The solution to our nutritional problems is probably to inspire and educate people to cook fresh, inexpensive food more often partly because its likely to be nicer and better for you but also, crucially, that it is only when you handle ingredients yourself that you understand the amount of fat, salt and sugar going into it. But let's not underestimate the enormity of this task. Writers, TV presenters, and mums and dads across the country have been plugging away at this for years, but kids and adults alike are still obsessed with chips and pizzas, and that canned meatloaf still flies off the shelves.

Of course, cheap food doesn't need to mean bad food. Over the last 18 months, food prices rose significantly and, at the same time, many had to survive on lower incomes. But to help people out, a plethora of books and TV shows appeared (or, as in the case of Delia's *Frugal Food*, resurrected). They reminded everyone of what they knew, deep down: that there are lots of fine foods that are cheap, such as beef shin, legumes, root veg – well, most veg, to be honest – and undervalued protein sources like mackerel, and it just takes an extra level of thought, a little planning and some extra time to turn these into bloody great dishes. Braised shin of beef is one of life's great joys – a gourmet's delight – yet it's made using one of the cheapest cuts of meats in the butchers.

Simple answers

So what's the solution to this fear and ignorance? Inspiration, fascination and enjoyment. We all need to cook better food more often, to understand nutrition and food science a little better, and broaden our diets to include as many different foods as possible. Nutritional finger wagging and government leaflets fail to connect with most people, so we need to find new ways to inspire and explain. Perhaps a TV series about the science of Es?

I make a kids' series for the BBC, called 'Gastronuts', that turns food into an adventure and shows kids that cooking is fascinating, that trying new food is cool and that getting away from their usual pizzas, chips and burgers can be seriously good fun. It might be a little kerr-azy for you, but at some level it seems to be working – I get emails from parents telling me how adventurous kids have become with their food, and this has resulted in a healthier diet without the word 'nutrition' ever being involved. It's early days, but it might help a little bit. If you have a better idea, please give me a bell because real solutions are few and far between.

In the final analysis, the best you can do for a healthy life is to be fascinated by food and flavour, know a little about nutrition, buy food fresh when you can and eat as many different types of it as possible, *including* food made with E numbers. Remember that everything on earth can kill you if you eat enough of it, but you also need a wide range of foods for a healthy metabolism. Be concerned about your food, but unless you're one of those unfortunate 0.01–0.23% of people with a real intolerance to food additives, don't worry unduly about Es because the risk they pose to health is infinitesimally small in comparison to the threats from poverty, obesity, unbalanced diets, excessive sunshine, physical inactivity, food poisoning, excessive consumption of alcohol and smoking. Even then, I am painfully aware that eating all those delicious saturated fatty, salty, sugary foods and lovely wine may be unhealthy but still lead to a happy life. Don't eat too much rubbish, have fun with your food, and *please* teach your kids to cook.

The big list of Es

Key:

🍎   = Es that occur naturally in food

🧍   = Es that our bodies create independently

E100
Curcumin; CI natural yellow 3;
Turmeric yellow; Diferoyl methane (Colour)

Let's not start off on the wrong foot. Curcumin is extracted from turmeric, a spice belonging to the ginger family, and it's been claimed to be effective as a treatment for an extraordinary range of problems, including cancer, Alzheimer's Disease, stroke and hypertrophy. But just because these have been claimed, it would be falling into the hands of the nutritional fruitcakes to hold this up as proof of anything, just as extravagant claims have been made for MSG intolerance, despite the lack of solid clinical evidence.

Many Es have been reported to cause problems, but clinical studies fail to verify them, however we should be wary of the opposite – curcumin health claims. Although there are hints, connections and reports about potential, the evidence doesn't seem to add up to much more than the basic facts that it *may* have antioxidant, anti-tumour and free-radical scavenging actions. And although these words are good to throw around in coffee-shop conversation, as any medical doctor will tell you, antioxidants can be a double-edged sword. As yet there is no solid evidence that curcumin will definitely stop stroke or heal your boils, although a lot of clinical studies are currently under way. And don't go thinking that because it's from a nice, friendly natural source that it's better for you – again, that would be playing into the hands of the anti-science brigade. Remember, friends, there's cyanide in apples. That doesn't make cyanide any cosier. Curcumin is a decent, useful additive, and that's pretty much it, until we hear otherwise.

Use: As well as its wide use as a natural colouring agent, turmeric is also a popular preservative in Asian food, due to its powerful antiseptic and antifungal properties. Its presence also helps to make food more digestible. Curcumin also helps prevent the colour of many food preparations, particularly pickles and relishes, from fading due to exposure to sunlight.

Source: This is the orangey-yellow pigment derived from the root of the turmeric plant (*Curcuma longa*). Turmeric is a widely used culinary spice, particularly in India, where it has long featured in most curry spice mixes. Turmeric is a member of the ginger family and has been widely cultivated across Asia for thousands of years, especially in India, China and Indonesia. As with ginger, it is the rhizome, or root-like stem, that is used, both fresh and dried then ground to a powder. Turmeric and curcumin can both now be produced artificially.

Likely products: Widely used in smoked white fish; baked products like cakes, biscuits and cereals, canned drinks and dairy products, especially ice creams, yoghurts, butter, margarine and cheeses.

Nutritional/medical benefits: Research into the low incidence of colo-rectal cancer among ethnic groups with a large intake of turmeric has discovered that it appears to have cancer-fighting properties. Trials of a turmeric-based anti-cancer drug are in progress. Some scientists also think that it can boost the brain function and has a future in the treatment of Alzheimer's and Parkinson's Disease.

Should you be scared of it? No, but there is some evidence that, as turmeric enhances the release of bile in the liver, high doses should not be taken by people with gallstones, jaundice, acute bilious colic or toxic liver disorders.

ADI (Acceptable Daily Intake): 0–3 mg/kg of body weight.

E101(i) ✦
Riboflavin; Lactoflavin; Vitamin B2; Riboflavin-5`-phosphate (Colour)

Bright lemon yellow or orange-yellow, this food colouring is also an important nutrient, Vitamin B2, and so may also be added to foods to fortify them.

Source: This occurs naturally in several types of food, notably dairy products, eggs, leafy green vegetables, liver and yeast, but the type found in these sources is readily broken down by exposure to light. The type used as an additive is generally synthesized from genetically modified *Bacillus subtilis*, a bacterium found in the soil and noted for it stimulating effect on the immune system.

Likely products: Widely found in baby foods, vitamin-enriched dairy products and breakfast cereals, such as Kellogg's Rice Krispies, Crunchy Nut, Frosties and Coco Pops; it is also common in commercial sauces, fruit drinks and processed cheeses. Obviously the vitamin is also widely used in nutritional supplements.

Nutritional/medical benefits: This water-soluble vitamin is essential for human health. Like the other B vitamins, it is required for energy production by aiding in the metabolism of fats, carbohydrates and proteins. It is also required for red blood cell formation and respiration, the production of antibodies to fight off disease, and for regulating human growth and reproduction. Healthy eyes, skin, nails and hair growth also require its action, as does the proper functioning of the thyroid gland.

Should you be scared of it? No. Quite the opposite – you need it in your diet, and without it you can get riboflavin deficiency, whose various symptoms including growth reduction in children and the glamorously named condition *scrotal dermatitis*.

ADI (Acceptable Daily Intake): 0–0.5 mg/kg of body weight.

E101(ii) ✎
Riboflavin-5`-phosphate, sodium (Colour)

This is mostly a monosodium salt produced by chemical action on E101(i), which becomes free riboflavin in the body. As with E101(i), it is used as a yellow colorant and vitamin supplement.

Use: In foods for infants and the young, as well as dairy products, preserves and confectionery.

Should you be scared of it? No, see E101(i).

ADI (Acceptable Daily Intake): 0–0.5 mg/kg of body weight.

E102
Tartrazine; CI food yellow 4; FD&C yellow no. 5 (Colour)

This is a water-soluble synthetic bright lemon yellow azo (nitrogen-based) dye, one of the notorious Southampton Six colours (see page 46).

Likely products: Many fruit drinks and coloured fizzy drinks; a wide range of convenience foods, including instant puddings and cake mixes, custard powder, packet soups and sauces; mustards and pickles; ice cream and lollies; marzipan; jams, jellies and marmalades; yoghurts; many glycerine, honey and lemon products. Mixed with E133 (Brilliant Blue FCF), it is responsible for the very particular green of tinned processed peas.

Food scares: Of all the azo dyes, it is assumed to be the one responsible for the most allergic reactions, particularly among asthmatics and those intolerant of aspirin. It can cause migraine and blurred vision, itching, rhinitis and skin discoloration.

Should you be scared of it? Possibly, if you suffer from one of the conditions above, or if you are concerned that your children show signs of hyperactivity after eating it. While still widely used in the UK the FSA recommends that you avoid giving children this colour if they show signs of hyperactivity and its use is banned in several European countries. It is one of the Southampton Six (see page 46) food colourings, on which the UK Food Standards Agency persuaded the British Government to propose a voluntary ban by the end of 2009. Also EU proposals for new legislation on food additives require that food containing any of these six colours should carry additional label information that 'consumption may have an adverse effect on activity and attention in children'. This requirement is likely to come into force around the middle of 2010.

ADI (Acceptable Daily Intake): 0–7.5 mg/kg of body weight.

E104
Quinoline yellow; CI food yellow (Colour)

A water-soluble synthetic dye made from coal tar and varying in colour between a greenish yellow and a darkish yellow. It's one of the notorious Southampton Six colorants (see page 46).

Use: It is often used to mimic the colour of lemons, limes and the green of pineapples, and is much used in tandem with other dyes to produce a wide range of tints. It is frequently used to colour medicines.

Likely products: Ices and desserts; soft drinks; scotch eggs; smoked white fish; jams and preserves; confectionery; sauces and seasonings.

Food scares: It has been reported to cause numbness, urticaria, watery eyes and rhinitis, and to increase the intake of aluminium by the body beyond the tolerable weekly limit.

Should you be scared of it? Possibly. It is one of the six food colours subject to a voluntary ban in the UK and likely to have to carry a warning regarding consumption by children by the end of 2010, see E102. It is banned in many countries, including Australia, the USA and Japan and the FSA recommends that you avoid giving it to children if they show signs of hyperactivity.

ADI (Acceptable Daily Intake): 0–0.5 mg/kg of body weight.

E110
Sunset Yellow FCF; Orange Yellow S;
CI food yellow 3; FD&C yellow no. 6 (Colour)

This is another synthetic orange yellow azo dye made from coal tar and used in fermented foods in which the dye must withstand heat treatment. It is often used in conjunction with other colours. It's one of the notorious Southampton Six colorants (see page 46).

Likely products: Lots of convenience foods, such as packet soups and sauces, pickles and canned fish; fruit squashes and jellies; ice creams; jams and marmalades; marzipan and confectionery.

Food scares: Another dye held to be the cause of a wide range of allergic reactions, particularly among those intolerant of aspirin, including urticaria, rhinitis and nasal congestion, allergies, hyperactivity, kidney tumours, chromosomal damage, abdominal pain, nausea and vomiting, indigestion, distaste for food; and increased incidence of tumours in animals. It has also been linked with hyperactive behaviour in children.

Should you be scared of it? Possibly, if you suffer from one of the conditions above. Also, while it is still widely used in the UK, the FSA recommends that you avoid giving children this colour if they show signs of hyperactivity. It is banned in several European countries including Norway and Finland, and is another of the six food colours subject to a voluntary ban in the UK and likely to have to carry a warning regarding consumption by children by the end of 2010, see E102.

ADI (Acceptable Daily Intake): 0–2.5 mg/kg of body weight.

E120
Cochineal; Carminic acid; Carmines (Colour)

Just outside Oaxaca in Mexico lies a strange farm. A very strange farm indeed. From afar it looks like a series of tatty cactus fields – perhaps a tequila distillery – but on closer inspection, the cacti are all covered in a white fluff, concealing lots of small bugs. These bugs are cochineal insects, and they are the source of one of my favourite E numbers.

Cochineal is a scale insect with an intense purple colour that's processed and then used in many famous foods, including M&Ms, liquorice allsorts, meats, drinks, jams and most pink marshmallows.

It has been used as a powerful dye since Aztec and Mayan times. The early Spanish settlers exported the natural crimson dye to Europe (it was then Mexico's second most valuable export after silver), where it became highly prized for regal, ceremonial and religious garb. The bugs are farmed by infecting cacti with cochineals and then protecting them for 3 months from cold, damp and predators. They are harvested by being individually knocked off the cactus at about 90 days old.

Why do food manufacturers use the juice of crushed beetles? Because cochineal is soluble in water and it's highly stable (it doesn't fade easily), and oddly enough, it's considered an organic additive as opposed to an artificial additive (it's only artificial once it's been purified into carmine). I have a bag of cochineal here in my office and I love grinding down a few bugs in a mortar and pestle and adding them to water – you only need two tiny bugs to turn a pint of water purple.

You may find it odd or even repulsive to eat insects, but they are an extremely important food source for many, and bear this in mind: there are 40 tonnes of insects for every human on the planet. Insects are highly nutritious and very efficient at turning plant matter into edible protein. In an ever-more populous and hungry world, we are very likely to start seeing these as an important food source in the near future.

Use: Cochineal is one of the few water-soluble colorants that do not readily fade with time. It is one of the most stable and oxidation-resistant of all the natural colorants – even more than many synthetic food colours.

Source: It is made from the crushed dried bodies of the cochineal insect, *Dactylopius coccus cacti L*, which feeds on cacti in the subtropical Americas. The colorant is the carminic acid in the insects (up to 24% of their body weight), which is there to help fend off predators.

Likely products: The water-soluble form, carminic acid, is used in alcoholic and soft drinks while calcium carmine, the insoluble form, is used in a wider variety of products. Together with ammonium carmine, they can be found in alcoholic drinks; baked products; biscuits; desserts; drinks; icings; pie fillings; some hard cheeses; sauces and sweets.

Food scares: A small number of people have been found to have allergies to carmine, with its effects ranging from mild cases of hives to anaphylactic shock. It has also been found to cause asthma in some people (see http://www.inchem.org/documents/jecfa/jecmono/v46je03.htm).

Should you be scared of it? Possibly. Sensitivity is rare, but you can be allergic to it. It is also derived from insects, so, if you are a vegetarian or follow certain religious dietary rules, you might want to avoid it.

ADI (Acceptable Daily Intake): 0–5 mg/kg of body weight.

E122
Azorubine; Carmoisine; CI food red 3 (Colour)

A synthetic bluish-red azo dye suitable for use in fermented foods that need to be heat-treated. It's one of the notorious Southampton Six colorants (see page 46).

Likely products: Convenience foods, such as packet soups, jellies and cheesecake mixes, raspberry- and blackcurrant-flavoured foods such as soft drinks, yoghurts; ices like Ice Berger Ice Pop; jams and preserves and confectionery.

Food scares: Another dye held to be the cause of allergic and/or intolerance reactions, including nettle rash and water retention, particularly among those intolerant of aspirin, and it has also been linked to hyperactivity in children. It is another of the six food colours subject to a voluntary ban in the UK and likely to have to carry a warning regarding consumption by children by the end of 2010, see E102.

Should you be scared of it? Possibly, if you suffer from one of the conditions above. Also, the FSA recommends that you avoid giving children this colour if they show signs of hyperactivity. It is currently banned in the USA, Japan, Norway and Sweden.

ADI (Acceptable Daily Intake): 0–4 mg/kg of body weight.

E123
Amaranth; CI food red 9; FD&C Red 2 (Colour)

This is a synthetic azo dye made from coal tar and named after the natural deep-red dye obtained from the small herbaceous plants called amaranth.

Likely products: Used when a purplish-red berry colour is needed, say for blackcurrants, this is also found in things like pie fillings; ice cream, jellies, trifles and jams, but more surprisingly in packet gravy and soups as well as prawns. It is also responsible for the particular lurid colour of glacé cherries.

Food scares: Can cause allergic and/or intolerance reactions, similar to nettle rash, particularly amongst asthmatics and those who have an aspirin intolerance. It can bring on asthma, eczema and hyperactivity. Based on some tests on female rats that showed a significant increase in cases of cancer, the USFDA (US Food and Drug Administration) banned it in 1976, although their spokesman said that they had found 'no evidence of a public health hazard'.

Should you be scared of it? Yes, if you're a massive consumer of glacé cherries or caviar, for the reasons above. It is banned in the USA, Austria, Norway and Russia. In Italy and France it is allowed only in caviar. A European Directive aims to restrict its use to alcoholic drinks and fish roe.

ADI (Acceptable Daily Intake): 0–0.5 mg/kg of body weight.

E124
Ponceau 4R; Cochineal Red A; CI food red 7; Brilliant Scarlet 4R; New coccine (Colour)

This is a synthetic bright red azo dye made from coal tar. It is one of the notorious Southampton Six colorants (see page 46).

Likely products: This is used in cheese rinds; cured meats; seafood dressings; soups; tinned strawberries; fruit pie fillings; trifles and many dessert toppings.

Food scares: Can cause allergic and/or intolerance reactions, particularly amongst asthmatics and those with aspirin intolerance, and it may cause hyperactivity in children. The EFSA lowered its ADI in 2009 in response to the discovery that it caused increase in migration of nuclear DNA in glandular, stomach, bladder and colon tissue, as well as changes in the bone marrow, which could be linked with cancer.

Should you be scared of it? Possibly, if you suffer from one of the conditions above. Also, the FSA recommends that you avoid giving children this colour if they show signs of hyperactivity. It is banned in the USA and Norway, and although it is not banned in the EU, its use is subject to strict quantitative limits in soft drinks, ices, confectionery, desserts and cheese. It is another of the six food colours subject to a voluntary ban in the UK and likely to have to carry a warning regarding consumption by children by the end of 2010, see E102.

ADI (Acceptable Daily Intake) 0–4 mg/kg of body weight.

E127
Erythrosine; CI food red 14; FD&C red no. 3 (Colour)

A light red/cherry-pink synthetic dye made from coal tar.

Likely products: Its most familiar use is as the colouring in tinned maraschino cherries. As well as in other preserved fruit, it is used in processed meats and salmon and crab spreads; snack foods like scotch eggs; in packet desserts and to colour pistachio nutshells.

Food scares: The molecules contain iodine, which is released if exposed to high heats. This has been linked to cases of thyroid malfunction, but the concentrations required for this cannot be reached through the consumption of food (http://www.food-info.net/uk/e/e127.htm). The dye has also been suspected of causing sensitivity to light and was also shown to cause cancer in tests on rats.

Nutritional/medical benefits: Used by dentists in tablets to reveal plaque.

Should you be scared of it? Possibly – if you have a sensitivity to sunlight or are worried about hyperactivity. It is banned in the USA and Norway, and a EU directive aims to restrict its use to colouring cherries.

ADI (Acceptable Daily Intake): 0–0.1 mg/kg of body weight.

E129
Allura Red AC; CI food red 17; FD&C red no. 40 (Colour)

An orange-red azo dye synthesized in the early '80s in order take the place of Amaranth (E123), which was being banned in several countries. It is one of the notorious Southampton Six colours (see page 46).

Likely products: Condiments; soft drinks; confectionery; ices and desserts.

Food scares: Thought to be less of an allergy/intolerance risk than the other azo dyes, it has still been linked to incidence of cancer in mice. It is not recommended for consumption by children and is another of the six food colours subject to a voluntary ban in the UK and likely to have to carry a warning regarding consumption by children by the end of 2010, see E102.

Should you be scared of it? Possibly, especially if you have sensitive skin. The FSA recommends that you avoid giving children this colour if they show signs of hyperactivity. It is banned in many European countries.

ADI (Acceptable Daily Intake): 0–7 mg/kg of body weight.

E131
Patent Blue V; CI food blue 5 (Colour)

A bright bluish-violet synthetic dye made from coal tar.

Likely products: Not widely used, but features in baked goods and confectionery, plus (curiously) Scotch eggs.

Food scares: Linked to allergic reactions, notably skin problems, low blood pressure, tremors and difficulty in breathing.

Nutritional/medical benefits: Used by doctors to colour lymph vessels.

Should you be scared of it? Possibly, particularly if prone to allergies and/or with sensitive skin. It is banned in the USA, Australia and Norway.

ADI (Acceptable Daily Intake): None allocated.

E132
Indigotine; Indigo Carmine; CI food blue 1; FD&C blue no. 2 (Colour)

A dark bluish-red synthetic dye made from coal tar using a process invented in the late nineteenth century after the discovery of the chemical structure of indigo. It is mostly used in combination with other food colours.

Likely products: Mainly baked goods, ices and confectionery.

Food scares: Linked with allergic reactions, including skin problems, high blood pressure and breathing problems.

Nutritional/medical benefits: This is a popular colorant in medicinal tablets and capsules, and is used by doctors in urine samples to check kidney function.

Should you be scared of it? Possibly, as discussed above. It is banned in Norway.

ADI (Acceptable Daily Intake): 0–5 mg/kg of body weight.

E133
Brilliant Blue FCF; CI food blue 2; FD&C blue no. 1 (Colour)

A greenish-blue synthetic dye made from coal tar and often used with E102 (tartrazine) or E104 (quinoline yellow) to achieve different shades of green, and with other food colours to produce browns and blacks.

Likely products: Found in soft drinks; canned and baked goods; confectionery such as M&Ms; ices and desserts.

Food scares: It is linked to some allergic reactions in asthmatics

Should you be scared of it? Possibly, if you are prone to asthma, as above. It has in the past been banned by a very wide range of countries but has more recently been certified as safe by the EU and the USA.

ADI (Acceptable Daily Intake) 0–5 mg/kg of body weight.

E140 🍎

Chlorophylls (CI natural green 3; Magnesium chlorophyll; Magnesium phaeophytin) and Chlorophyllins (Chlorophyllin; CI natural green 5; Sodium chlorophyllin; Potassium chlorophyllin) (Colour)

Chlorophylls are oil-soluble natural green dyes; chlorophyllins are a water-soluble version of them made by the same sort of process that turns fats into soap.

Source: Chlorophylls are natural pigments present in all green leafy vegetables. The food colorants are usually extracted from cheaper edible plant material such as grass, alfalfa and nettles.

Natural version: All green leafy vegetables.

Likely products: Used in soups and processed green vegetables; confectionery; yoghurts; ices; fats and oils.

Food scares: None known.

Nutritional/medical benefits: Used to colour some medicines.

Should you be scared of it? No, these are all considered to be completely safe, so have no recommended maximum daily intake.

ADI (Acceptable Daily Intake): Unlimited.

E141

Copper complexes of Chlorophylls (CI natural green 3; Copper chlorophyll; Copper phaeophytin) and chlorophyllins (CI natural green 5; Sodium copper chlorophyllin; Potassium copper chlorophyllin) (Colour)

Chemically modified versions of the natural green colours E140. The water-soluble version is green and the oil-soluble one olive-green. They are brighter and more stable than their all-natural counterparts.

Source: Made by adding a copper salt to the extract of plant material used to make E140.

Likely products: Confectionery; yoghurts; ices; jams; some cheeses; pickles and processed green vegetables and sauces.

Food scares: None.
Should you be scared of it? No.
ADI (Acceptable Daily Intake) 0–15 mg/kg of body weight.

E142
Green S; CI food green 4; Brilliant green BS (Colour)

A greenish-blue synthetic dye made from coal tar that is mostly used in combination with other colours, such as E102 (tartrazine) and E104 (quinoline yellow), to make particular shades of green, and with others to produce browns and blacks.

Likely products: Mostly used in tinned peas and soft drinks, as well as convenience items such as gravy granules; mint jelly and sauce; packet breadcrumbs; cake mixes and ice creams.
Food scares: Thought to be a factor in causing allergic reactions such as asthma, urticaria, insomnia and hyperactivity.
Should you be scared of it? Possibly, for the reasons above. It is banned in the USA, Canada, Japan and most Scandinavian countries.
ADI (Acceptable Daily Intake): 0–5 mg/kg of body weight.

E150a ♣
Plain caramel (Colour)

A natural food colour, ranging in shade from dark-red through to dark-browns and blacks. This and the three variations that follow are by far the most widely used food colours.

Source: Made by heating various types of sugar under pressure.
Natural version: As one would make caramel at home by heating sugar in a heavy pan.
Likely products: Beer and wines; vinegars; soft drinks (particularly Coca-Cola); gravies and sauces; pickles; meat products; brown bread; potato crisps; baked products and convenience desserts and confectionery.
Should you be scared of it? No.
ADI (Acceptable Daily Intake): Not specified.

E150b
Caustic sulphite caramel (Colour)

A version of caramel food colouring treated with alkalis to suit particular types of foods.

Source: Made by heating various types of sugar under pressure and then treating the results with chemicals.

Likely products: Mostly spirits; flavour extracts such as coffee and vanilla; salted meats; soups ands sauces.

Should you be scared of it? No.

ADI (Acceptable Daily Intake): 0–160 mg/kg of body weight.

E150c
Ammonia caramel (Colour)

A version of caramel food colouring treated with ammonia to suit particular types of foods.

Source: Made by heating various types of sugar under pressure and then treating the results with ammonia.

Likely products: Particularly beers; synthetic soy and other dark sauces and confectionery.

Should you be scared of it? No.

ADI (Acceptable Daily Intake) 0–160 mg/kg of body weight.

E150d
Sulphite ammonia caramel (Colour)

A version of caramel food colouring treated with sulphite and ammonia to suit particular types of foods.

Source: Made by heating various types of sugar under pressure and then treating the results with chemicals.

Likely products: Mostly soft drinks, but also found in some snack foods such as Monster Munch Pickled Onion flavour and Bacon Flavour Fries.

Should you be scared of it? No.
ADI (Acceptable Daily Intake): 0–150 mg/kg of body weight.

E151
Brilliant Black BN; Black BN; CI food black 1 (Colour)

A violet–black synthetic dye made from coal tar.

Likely products: Fish roe products; mustard; jams; sauces; soft drinks; soups and sweets.

Food scares: It appears to cause or intolerance reactions, particularly amongst those with intolerance, and may worsen the symptoms of asthma.

Should you be scared of it? Possibly, as discussed above. It is also banned in the USA, Canada, Japan, Australia and many European countries.

ADI (Acceptable Daily Intake): 0–1 mg/kg of body weight.

E153 ◕
Vegetable carbon (Colour)

This natural black colouring is made by burning all sorts of organic material, as well as oil and gas, at high temperature in the absence of air, but the most common source is vegetable in origin, usually peat.

Natural version: Burnt toast, etc.

Likely products: Confectionery, especially licorice; jams and jellies.

Food scares: This was at one time thought possibly to be carcinogenic, and its use was banned in the USA for that reason. However, experts are now coming to the opinion that this effect may have been due to impurities.

Should you be scared of it? No, but be aware of the above.

ADI (Acceptable Daily Intake): None allocated.

E154
Brown FK; Kipper Brown; CI food brown 1 (Colour)

A mixture of several synthetic azo dyes and other chemicals that produces a reddish-brown dye.

Likely products: Its use is limited by law to kippers only in the UK.

Food scares: It can provoke allergic reactions in some people sensitive to aspirin, and can intensify the symptoms of asthma.

Should you be scared of it? Possibly. It is banned in the EU, except the UK, and in Australia, Canada, Japan and the USA.

ADI (Acceptable Daily Intake): None allocated.

E155
Brown HT; CI food brown 3; Chocolate brown HT (Colour)

This is a synthetic reddish-brown azo dye made from coal tar.

Likely products: Baked goods and confectionery, usually with chocolate.

Food scares: Can produce skin sensitivity and linked with allergic reactions, especially among asthmatics and those intolerant to aspirin.

Should you be scared of it? Possibly, if you are asthmatic or intolerant to aspirin. It is banned in the USA, Australia and many European countries.

ADI (Acceptable Daily Intake): 0–1.5 mg/kg of body weight.

E160a ♥
Carotenes; CI food orange 5 (Colour)

Natural orange or yellow pigments.

Source: Found in many types of brightly coloured vegetables, especially carrots, green leafy vegetables and tomatoes. It can be synthesized, but the natural version is cheaper to make and thus much more widely used

Natural version: Brightly coloured vegetables.

Likely products: Many foods, including yellow fats and dairy products; San Marco Americano Pizzas; beverages and soft drinks, confectionery.

Nutritional/medical benefits: Carotenes are turned into vitamin A by the body.
Should you be scared of it? No.
ADI (Acceptable Daily Intake): Current levels are acceptable.

:::

E160b 🍎
Annatto; Bixin; Norbixin; CI natural orange (Colour)
A natural orangey colouring that can be used to give yellow, peach or red hues to food.

Source: This is derived from the seeds of the achiote or roucou tree (*Bixa orellana L*), native to South and Central America. The pigment derived from the oil in their seeds is also known as annatto and bixin. Chemical treatment produces from it a water-soluble version called norbixin. In America, people have used annatto as a dye and flavouring for centuries.
Likely products: Mainly yellow fats and oils; cheeses; smoked fish; mayonnaise; convenience foods like instant mashed potato, pie pastry, Birds Eye Chicken Pies, potato crisps, Quavers and Wotsits, fish fingers, soft drinks and desserts.
Food scares: Despite it being a natural product that could actually be nutritionally valuable (see below), it has been linked to cases of food-related allergy, but has been used as a foodstuff in America for many generations.
Nutritional/medical benefits: Annatto is one of the vegetable pigments known as carotenoids that have been recognized as having significant health-giving properties. They are antioxidants, so counter potentially damaging free radicals in the body and lower cholesterol levels, so help fight heart disease. Many also have significant anti-cancer properties. There is strong scientific evidence that annatto is an antimicrobial, and that it lowers cholesterol levels and protects the liver. In Latin America, although it is recognized that some people are highly sensitive to it, it is commonly taken as a digestive stimulant and used to treat hypertension and prostate and urinary problems.
Should you be scared of it? Not really, but in the UK and EU its use as a colorant is limited to a prescribed range of foods in specific quantitative limits.
ADI (Acceptable Daily Intake): A temporary ADI was withdrawn in 2006.

E160c ♣
Paprika extract; Paprika oleoresin; Capsanthian; Capsorubin (Colour)

This is another natural deep orangey colouring.

Use: As well as being a popular colorant, paprika is also a familiar spice and ingredient in many classic dishes.

Source: This is derived from sweet red peppers, *Capsicum annuum*. Because it has a distinctive flavour, it is mostly used in cases where this will also enhance the food being coloured. Paprika is actually made up of two actual pigments, capsorubin and capsanthin.

Natural version: The flesh of sweet red peppers.

Likely products: Soups; sauces; pickles; meat and poultry products; and seasonings. It is used in poultry feed to deepen the colour of egg yolks. Use of paprika as a colorant is increasing as manufacturers move away from problematic synthetic colours.

Nutritional/medical benefits: The two constituent pigments, capsorubin and capsanthin are carotenoids (see E160b) and recent studies would seem to indicate that they are particularly powerful antioxidants.

Should you be scared of it? No.

ADI (Acceptable Daily Intake): None allocated.

E160d ♣
Lycopene; CI natural yellow 27 (Colour)

Another natural dye.

Use: To give orange and red colours to food.

Source: This is the pigment in red tomatoes and is made by extracting it from them by means of a solvent.

Natural version: Red tomatoes. Heinz tomato ketchup says on the label 'Naturally contains Lycopene (8.5mg per 100g)'.

Likely products: Soups, sauces and many other savoury products.

Nutritional/medical benefits: Lycopene is a carotenoid (see E160b) and has been shown to have a beneficial effect on the heart, blood pressure, prostate, osteoporosis, the skin and other areas. It is also held by many to have a powerfully anti-cancer effect, but research is still underway on this.

Should you be scared of it? No.
ADI (Acceptable Daily Intake): 0–0.5mg/kg of body weight.

E160e 🍎
Beta-apo-8'-carotenal (C30); CI food orange 6 (Colour)

An orangey-red colour that, although the natural pigment in some citrus fruits, is mostly synthesized as the 'nature identical' apocarotenal for use as an additive.

Use: To give orange and red colours to food.
Natural version: Oranges and tangerines.
Likely products: Soft drinks; yellow fats; confectionery such as M&Ms, soups; sauces; salad dressings; cheese slices; ices and desserts.
Nutritional/medical benefits: This is yet another carotenoid (see E160b) and is used by the body to make vitamin A.
Should you be scared of it? No.
ADI (Acceptable Daily Intake): 0–5 mg/kg of body weight.

E160f
Ethyl ester of beta-apo-8'-carotenoic acid; CI food orange 7; beta-apo-8' carotenic ester (Colour)

Although another carotenoid, this is only available commercially as a synthetic red-to-violet crystalline compound used.

Use: To give orange and red colours to food.
Likely products: Rarely used.
Nutritional/medical benefits: This is yet another carotenoid (see E160b).
Should you be scared of it? No.
ADI (Acceptable Daily Intake): 0–5 mg/kg of body weight.

E161b 🍎
Lutein (Colour)
Another natural dye.

Use: To give a yellow colour to food.

Source: Obtained by solvent extraction from a wide range of edible fruits and plants, including marigolds and alfalfa.

Likely products: Citrus drinks; confectionery; marzipan and mayonnaise. Used in poultry farming to enhance the colour of egg yolks and the chickens themselves (lutein is, in fact, one of the pigments that gives chicken their colour).

Nutritional/medical benefits: This is yet another carotenoid (see E160b). Lutein is important to eye function and is often prescribed to those in danger of age-related eye problems, such as cataracts and macular degeneration, and added to dietary supplements for this reason. Lutein may also help prevent or slow down atherosclerosis, the thickening of arteries, which is a major risk for cardiovascular disease

Should you be scared of it? No, although note that excess consumption can cause bronzing of the skin.

ADI (Acceptable Daily Intake): 0–2 mg/kg of body weight.

E161g 🍎
Canthaxanthin; CI food orange 8 (Colour)
A natural orange, although much of it is now made commercially from beta-carotene (see E160e).

Use: To give orange to violet-red colouring to food.

Source: This is a natural pigment derived from salmon, trout and crustaceans, as well as some fungi and flamingo feathers.

Likely products: Used in fish and poultry farming to add colour to flesh, skin and eggs. Found in fish fingers; pickles; sauces; preserves and sweets. Famously, it is the color used in saucisse de Strasbourg.

Food scares: Its use in suntan products was found possibly to exacerbate eye problems, and notably diminished low-light vision. Although such products use a much higher concentration of it, there is still some concern, hence its low ADI.

Nutritional/medical benefits: This is yet another carotenoid (see E160b).

Should you be scared of it? No, in recommended low levels, see the note on eye problems above.

ADI (Acceptable Daily Intake): 0–0.3mg/kg of body weight.

E162 🍎
Beetroot Red; Beet red; Betanin (Colour)
A natural deep-red/purple colour.

Use: Mostly used to impart a pink hue to food to food.

Source: Extracted from red beetroots (*Beta vulgaris*) either by pressing them or soaking shredded roots. The pigment is due to betacyanins, of which betanin is the major component.

Natural version: Red beetroots.

Likely products: Mainly soft drinks and frozen and dried food, such as ice creams, dairy products, breakfast cereals, desserts and icings; confectionery especially licorice; also some tomato and meat products, especially sausages and bacon.

Food scares: Beetroot juice is high in nitrates, which can be a problem for babies and young children as these can interfere with the child's red blood cells ability carry oxygen around their body.

Nutritional/medical benefits: Betacyanins are antioxidants and several studies have shown that they are potentially effective in fighting cancer, particularly of the stomach and colon. They are also anti-inflammatory and help lower blood cholesterol, thus potent in helping prevent heart disease.

Should you be scared of it? No, but see note on nitrates above.

ADI (Acceptable Daily Intake): Not allocated.

E163 🍎
Anthocyanins; Grape skin extract; Grape colour extract; Enocianina (Colour)

These are natural red pigments.

Use: To give red or purple shades to foods.

Source: Extracted from many brightly coloured edible fruits, berries and vegetables, mostly grape skins but also sometimes elderberries, red cabbage and black carrots.

Natural version: Grapes, elderberries, red cabbage, etc.

Likely products: Soft drinks, such as Strawberry Fruit Shoots (Summer Fruits flavour), jams, jellies and fruit sauces; preserved fruit; dairy products especially yoghurts and confectionery.

Nutritional/medical benefits: Anthocyanins are powerful antioxidants and there is growing evidence that they have potential health benefits to protext against cancer, inflammation, diabetes, bacterial infections and even ageing.

Should you be scared of it? No.

ADI (Acceptable Daily Intake): None allocated.

E170 🍎
Calcium carbonate; CI pigment white 18 (Colour, raising agent, anti-caking agent, texturizer)

A synthetic white colouring.

Use: As well as being used as a food colouring, this also serves as a source of carbon dioxide in raising agents, as an anti-caking agent, a source of fortifying calcium and a texturizing agent in chewing gum.

Source: Calcium carbonate is a naturally occurring mineral found as chalk or limestone, eggshells, pearls and the shells of many marine species, but the food-grade mineral is made chemically.

Natural version: Chalk, limestone, eggshells, etc.

Likely products: Mainly in chewing gum; raising agents and bread, but also found in ice creams, cakes and sweets, canned fruit and vegetables.

Food scares: Unusually high levels of consumption of the mineral may produce flatulence, constipation, haemorrhoids and bleeding anal fissures; and long-term high levels could result in high levels in the blood, risking confusion, stomach pain, weakness and kidney stones.

Should you be scared of it? No, only at extremely high levels of consumption as above.

ADI (Acceptable Daily Intake): Unlimited.

E171 🍎
Titanium dioxide; CI pigment white 6 (Colour)

A natural bright white colouring in powder form, that accounts for 70% of the world's pigment manufacture. It is what is used to mark the lines at Wimbledon; it is used in place of snow for TV and film locations, and NASA paint rockets with it because of its high refractive index. It is also used to encourage medical implants to integrate with bone.

Use: As a white food colouring, to make liquids opaque and to give a light background to other colours. In the case of skimmed milk, it has also been found to make it more palatable.

Source: Extracted from the heavy black metallic oxide mineral limonite.

Likely products: Confectionery such as M&Ms, ice cream, icings, skimmed milk and non-dairy creamers; cottage and mozzarella cheeses; horseradish cream and sauces.

Should you be scared of it? No. Titanium dioxide has been linked with cancer, but only when breathed in as a powder and not when ingested.

ADI (Acceptable Daily Intake): Unlimited.

E172 🍎
Iron oxide and hydroxides (Colour)

Natural pigments which range in colour from yellow, red and orange to black. Natural iron oxides pigments are called ochres. Many classic paint colours, such as raw and burnt siennas and umbers, are iron-oxide pigments.

Source: Manufactured by controlled oxidization of iron in the presence of water (rusting).

Natural version: Rust.

Likely products: Fish and meat pastes; canned foods; cake and dessert mixes and confectionery.

Food scares: Toxic in very high doses unlikely to be achieved from its uses as a food colouring.

Should you be scared of it? No.

ADI (Acceptable Daily Intake): 0–0.5 mg/kg body weight.

E173
Aluminium (Colour)

The metal element is used as a natural colouring used to give a bright metallic shine to the exterior of small decorative pieces of sugar confectionery to decorate cakes and pastries only.

Source: The 99% pure metal ground to a powder.

Likely products: Only as above.

Food scares: Evidence seems to indicate that an accumulation of aluminium in the nervous system could be toxic and it is found in abnormally high levels in the brain cells of those with Alzheimer's Disease, but it is not known if this is its cause or simply another symptom. There are also concerns about its possible effect on the reproductive system and the developing nervous systems of the young. A small percentage of people do have an response to the ingestion of aluminium and experience digestive disorders, or other symptoms.

Should you be scared of it? No, not to most people as a food additive in its currently permitted form (unless you eat an awful lot of those little metallic balls on cup cakes), but note the above.

ADI (Acceptable Daily Intake): None currently established.

E174
Silver (Colour)

The metal element is used as a natural colouring to give a bright metallic shine to the exterior of small decorative pieces of sugar confectionery, to decorate chocolates and in liqueurs only.

Source: The 99.5% pure metal is made into bars or wire (or silver leaf in the case of Indian *vark* used to decorate chocolates).

Likely products: Only as above.

Nutritional/medical benefits: Before the advent of antibiotics, silver was widely used as antibacterial, as it has strong antimicrobial and antifungal properties. Silver preparations are sold as natural remedies for all manner of ailments, especially kidney malfunction, but are regarded as unproven and unwise by medical experts.

Should you be scared of it? No, certainly not in the tiny quantities used.

ADI (Acceptable Daily Intake): Not allocated.

E175
Gold (Colour)

The dense yellow precious metal element is used as a natural colouring to give a bright golden appearance to the exterior of small decorative pieces of sugar confectionery, to decorate chocolates and in liqueurs only. Gold is good fun to use on food, although you've got to be careful otherwise your food can verge on the tasteless (in terms of style, I mean – it's always physically tasteless), so save it for extra special occasions like weddings or birthdays. It's often used in cooking in India (especially in sweets) and I've managed to use it to gild a whole chicken as well as lots of sausages – kids love eating golden sausages. You should always use the highest purity (over 23ct) gold leaf, and oddly enough it's not that expensive as it's so extraordinarily thin. Press each transfer leaf against a recently cooked chicken or roll a still-warm sausage over a leaf and the gold should be left behind. It's so thin that it never seems to affect your fillings like foil might, and it's fun to leave behind a few flecks on your lips. There is also a small likelihood that if you eat food covered in gold, you'll lay a golden egg, although I've never managed one yet.

Source: Food-grade gold is 99.99% pure, but it is permitted to be mixed with up to 7% silver or 4% copper in order to make it more malleable for the production of gold leaf. Added silver gives it a greenish hue, copper an orange tinge.

Likely products: As above.

Nutritional/medical benefits: Gold was once held to be medicinal but as it is now viewed as totally inert when metabolized this is unlikely, as is it's being in any way harmful.

Should you be scared of it? No.

ADI (Acceptable Daily Intake): Not allocated.

E180
Litholrubine BK; Pigment rubine; D&C red no 6 (Colour)

A bright red synthetic azo dye.

Likely products: Only cheeses (to colour the rinds).

Food scares: Those prone to asthma or allergies may find their symptoms exacerbated by consuming cheese rinds coloured with this additive.

Should you be scared of it? No, but see above.

ADI (Acceptable Daily Intake): None allocated.

E200 🍎
Sorbic acid (Preservative)

This occurs naturally in the unripe fruits of the rowan shrub (*Sorbus aucuparia L.*) and in some wines, although the substance used as a food preservative is synthetic and derived from the gas ketene.

Use: It's an antimicrobial, which means that it kills or inhibits the growth of bacteria, fungi or other microorganisms. E200 covers a wide range of these microorganisms, especially yeasts and moulds and aerobic bacteria. Sorbic acid and the two sorbates that follow (E202 and E203) are often used in combination with other preservatives.

Likely products: Baked goods; cider; non-alcoholic beverages; cheeses and dairy products; meat products; candied peel and sweets.

Nutritional/medical benefits: An antimicrobial, preventing food from spoiling and developing toxic potential.

Should you be scared of it? No.

ADI (Acceptable Daily Intake): 0–25 mg/kg body weight.

E202
Potassium sorbate (Preservative)
Made by chemical treatment of E200.

Use: As E200.
Likely products: As E200, plus concentrated fruit juice; energy drinks (such as Relentless); dried and candied fruit; olives; jams and preserves; margarine; pickles; processed cheese; convenience salad and seafood dressings, and wine.
Nutritional/medical benefits: As E200.
Should you be scared of it? No.
ADI (Acceptable Daily Intake): 0–25 mg/kg body weight.

E203
Calcium sorbate (Preservative)
Made by chemical treatment of E200.

Use: As E200.
Likely products: As E202.
Nutritional/medical benefits: As E200.
Should you be scared of it? No.
ADI (Acceptable Daily Intake): 0–25 mg/kg body weight.

E210
Benzoic acid; Flowers of benzoin; Phenylcarboxylic acid; Carboxybenzene (Preservative)
Although a natural pigment found in many edible berries, fruit and vegetables, the food grade version is a synthetic dye produced either from toluene, the solvent common in paints, or from benzoin, a resin from the bark of several types of Asian tree in the species *Styrax*.

Use: Very effective against yeasts and moulds but less so in the case of bacteria.

Natural version: Ripe cranberries, bilberries and cloudberries; plums; cultured dairy products and fermented cheeses and cinnamon.

Likely products: The most important preservative used in soft drinks. Also found in beers; cordials; coffee essences and flavouring essences; fruit syrups; pulps and purées; jams; pickles and relishes; marinated fish; baked goods; fruit yoghurts and cheeses.

Food scares: It can cause rashes and gastric irritation in those prone to allergies, and can cause asthma attacks in those on steroid asthma medication. Some believe that it is linked with behavioural disorders in children, and it is closely related to E211, which was implicated as part of the Southampton Six cocktail of additives known to increase the risk of hyperactivity in children (see page 46).

Nutritional/medical benefits: An antifungal and antimicrobial as above.

Should you be scared of it? Possibly, if you are prone to allergies or are on steroid asthma medication.

ADI (Acceptable Daily Intake): 0–5 mg/kg body weight.

E211
Sodium benzoate (Preservative)

This sodium salt of E210 (benzoic acid) is another synthetic preservative.

Use: As E210, but it is slightly more potent in action against bacteria, although it is effective only in slightly acid foods. It is also used to mask the taste of poor-quality foods.

Source: As E210.

Natural version: As E210.

Likely products: Mostly slightly acidic foods, such as pickled cucumbers, salad dressings, barbecue sauces, preserves, relishes and condiments; olives; fruit juices (orange juices can contain high amounts); lollipops; Ribena blackcurrant lollies; meat and dairy products and baked goods.

Food scares: Sodium benzoate combines with ascorbic acid (vitamin C) to produce the known carcinogen benzene. It was also one of the additives added to the mixes of colours used in the Southampton University studies of the effects of additives on children (see page 46) and is therefore not recommended for consumption by children. There is some evidence that those prone to asthma or allergies can have reactions to it, particularly when it is used in combination with E102 (tartrazine).

Nutritional/medical benefits: As E210.

Should you be scared of it? Possibly, as described above.

ADI (Acceptable Daily Intake): As E210.

E212
Potassium benzoate (Preservative)

This potassium salt of E210 (benzoic acid) is another synthetic preservative.

Use: As E210.

Source: As E210.

Natural version: As E210.

Likely products: Mainly in margarines, pickles, pineapple juice and olives

Food scares: There is some evidence that those prone to asthma or allergies can have reactions to it, particularly when it is used in combination with E102 (tartrazine).

Nutritional/medical benefits: As E210.

Should you be scared of it? Possibly, as discussed above.

ADI (Acceptable Daily Intake): As E210.

E213
Calcium benzoate (Preservative)

This calcium salt of E210 (benzoic acid) is another synthetic preservative.

Use: As E210.

Source: As E210.

Natural version: As E210.

Likely products: Mostly concentrated pineapple juice.

Food scares: As E212.

Should you be scared of it? Possibly, as discussed in E212.

ADI (Acceptable Daily Intake): AS E210.

E214
Ethyl p-hydroxybenzoate (Preservative)
Synthetic chemical preservative.

Use: Very effective against yeasts and moulds but less so in the case of bacteria.

Likely products: Permitted only in a limited range of snack foods, confectionery and pâtés.

Food scares: Can cause skin irritation, contact dermatitis and Rosacea in a small percentage of the general population.

Nutritional/medical benefits: An antifungal and antimicrobial as above.

Should you be scared of it? Possibly, as per the above.

ADI (Acceptable Daily Intake): 0–10 mg/kg body weight.

E215
Sodium ethyl p-hydroxybenzoate (Preservative)
As E214.

Use: As E214.

Likely products: As E214.

Food scares: As E214.

Nutritional/medical benefits: As E214.

Should you be scared of it? Possibly, as per E214.

ADI (Acceptable Daily Intake): As E214.

E218
Methyl p-hydroxybenzoate (Preservative)
As E214.

Use: As E214.

Likely products: As E214.

Food scares: As E214.

Nutritional/medical benefits: As E214.

Should you be scared of it? Yes, as per E214.

ADI (Acceptable Daily Intake): As E214.

E219
Sodium methyl p-hydroxybenzoate (Preservative)
As E214.

Use: As E214.
Likely products: As E214.
Food scares: As E214.
Nutritional/medical benefits: As E214.
Should you be scared of it? Yes, as per E214.
ADI (Acceptable Daily Intake): As E214.

E220 🍎
Sulphur dioxide (Preservative)
This additive is in almost every bottle of wine (that's why wine labels state 'contains sulphites'). As a food additive it is usually made from coal tar. All the additives numbered from E220–E228 (the others are salts of this one) are roughly similar when used in food and drinks.

Use: Sulphites are among the oldest preservatives used by man and were known to the Ancient Greeks and Romans. Indeed they have become essential ingredients in many traditional foods like wines and sausages.
Likely products: Soft drinks and fruit juices; fermented drinks, including wine, cider and perry; vinegar; dried fruits and vegetables; sausages and burgers; jams and biscuits.
Food scares: Can be toxic in large amounts, it is also thought to bring on asthma attacks in some people. It destroys vitamin B1 in the body and can reduce the vitamin levels in the food in which it is used. It can be difficult to metabolize for those with impaired kidney function.
Should you be scared of it? Possibly, if you are asthmatic or have impaired kidney function as above.
ADI (Acceptable Daily Intake): 0–0.7 mg/ kg body weight.

E221 🍎
Sodium sulphite (Preservative)

The sodium salt of sulphur dioxide, see E220.

Use: As E220.

Likely products: Fresh orange juice; dried fruit; refined sugar and preserved meats.

Food scares: As E220.

Should you be scared of it? Possibly, see E220.

ADI (Acceptable Daily Intake): See E220.

E222 🍎
Sodium hydrogen sulphite; Sodium bisulphate (Preservative)

A salt of sulphur dioxide, see E220, made by bubbling it in a solution of sodium carbonate in water.

Use: As E220.

Likely products: In almost all commercial wines and in canned fruit. Also sometimes sold as a proprietary preservative for fresh green vegetables for use in places like salad bars. This was common practice in the USA until the use of E222 was banned for use on raw fruit and vegetables after an incident in which 13 people died from an accidentally huge overdose in such circumstances.

Food scares: As E220.

Should you be scared of it? Possibly, see E220.

ADI (Acceptable Daily Intake): As E220.

E223 🍎

Sodium metabisulphite; Sodium pyrosulphite (Preservative)

A sodium salt of sulphur dioxide, see E220, made by bubbling it in a solution of sodium carbonate in water.

Use: As E220.

Likely products: Fruit juice concentrates and dried fruit; chocolate bars; vinegars and pickles; Walker's French Fries and Squares; Campden tablets for home wine- and beer-making.

Food scares: As E220. Also a skin and lung irritant.

Should you be scared of it? Possibly, see E220 and above.

ADI (Acceptable Daily Intake): As E220.

E224 🍎

Potassium metabisulphite (Preservative)

A potassium salt of sulphur dioxide, see E220.

Use: As E220.

Likely products: Fruit and fruit products; wine; shellfish and pickles.

Food scares: As E220. Excess exposure can cause cyanosis, faintness and even unconsciousness.

Should you be scared of it? Possibly, see E220 and above.

ADI (Acceptable Daily Intake): As E220.

E226 🍎

Calcium sulphite (Preservative)

A calcium salt of sulphur dioxide, see E220.

Use: As E220.

Likely products: Fruit and fruit products; cider and refined sugars.

Food scares: As E220. Can also be a gastric irritant.

Should you be scared of it? Possibly, see E220 and above.

ADI (Acceptable Daily Intake): As E220.

E227 ●

Calcium hydrogen sulphite; Calcium bisulphite (Preservative)

A calcium salt of sulphur dioxide, see E220.

Use: As E220.
Likely products: Beer.
Food scares: As E220.
Should you be scared of it? Possibly, see E220.
ADI (Acceptable Daily Intake): As E220.

E228 ●

Potassium hydrogen sulphite (Preservative)

A potassium salt of sulphur dioxide, see E220.

Use: As E220.
Likely products: Wine and acidic preserved fruits.
Food scares: As E220.
Should you be scared of it? Possibly, see E220 and above.
ADI (Acceptable Daily Intake): As E220.

E230

Biphenyl; diphenyl; phenylbenzene (Preservative)

A synthetic preservative made from the industrial solvent benzene.

Use: Predominantly against *Penicillium* fungi growing on citrus fruit.
Likely products: Mostly fruit, particularly citrus fruit. It is generally used in containers and on the wrappings of the fruit. However, the fruits are sometimes dipped in it and then the chemical may slowly permeate the fruit itself.
Food scares: It is an eye and skin irritant, but you really have to handle or be exposed to quite a lot of it for this to occur.
Should you be scared of it? No, but see above.
ADI (Acceptable Daily Intake): 0–0.05 mg/kg body weight.

E231
Orthophenyl phenol; phenylphenol; 2-phenylphenol; O-phenylphenol; Dowicide 1 (Preservative)

A synthetic antifungal made from phenyl ether and widely used in agriculture.

Likely products: Many fruits and vegetables (notably apples, pears, peaches, plums, pineapples, citrus fruits, cherries, nectarines, carrots, sweet potatoes, tomatoes and peppers) are treated with it after being harvested, leaving a residue on the skins.

Food scares: Some people are sensitive to the compound and it can cause skin irritation.

Should you be scared of it? No, but see above.

ADI (Acceptable Daily Intake): 0–0.2 mg/kg body weight.

E232
Sodium orthophenyl phenol; Dowicide A (Preservative)

The sodium salt of orthophenyl phenol is also used as an agricultural preservative.

Likely products: Citrus fruits, apples and pears. It is used to spray the fruit so may eventually penetrate the skin and get into the flesh.

Should you be scared of it? No.

ADI (Acceptable Daily Intake): 0–0.2 mg/kg body weight.

E234
Nisin (Preservative)

A natural antimicrobial peptide (small protein).

Use: A strong antibacterial but with little antifungal effect, it is particularly effective against *Listeria* and spore-forming microbes such as *Clostridium* and *Baccillus*. It is thus an important preservative in foods that are pasteurized but not fully sterilized.

Source: It is produced by certain strains of the lactic acid bacterium *Lactococcus lactis* subsp. *Lactis* normally used in cheese production.

Natural version: Cheeses.

Likely products: Pasteurized processed cheeses and dairy products; pasteurized liquid egg products; canned vegetables; tomato paste; some Continental sausages; sauces and salad dressings and beer.

Nutritional/medical benefits: An antibacterial.

Should you be scared of it? No.

ADI (Acceptable Daily Intake): 0–33000 units/kg body weight.

E235
Natamycin; Pimaricin; Tennectin (Preservative)

An extremely potent natural antifungal, with little or no antibacterial effect.

Use: As it has low solubility in water it is very effective for surface treatment of foods.

Source: It is made from *Streptomycetes* bacteria found everywhere in the soil.

Likely products: Mostly cheeses, such as cottage cheese, sour cream and yoghurt, dried cured sausages.

Nutritional/medical benefits: Used to treat fungal infections and candidiasis.

Should you be scared of it? No.

ADI (Acceptable Daily Intake): 0–0.3 mg/kg body weight.

E239
Hexamethylene tetramine; Hexamine; Methenamine; Cystamine (Preservative)

A little-used synthetic compound made by the reaction of formaldehyde and ammonia.

Use: The compound functions as an antibacterial by releasing formaldehyde.

Likely products: Cheese – its use is permitted only in Provolone, an Italian hard cheese.

Nutritional/medical benefits: Used to treat infections of the lower urinary tract and obstructive post-renal disease.
Should you be scared of it? No.
ADI (Acceptable Daily Intake): 0–0.15 mg/kg body weight.

E242
Dimethyl dicarbonate; DMDC (Preservative)
A synthetic chemical that is not a preservative in the traditional sense but rather a cold sterilant.

Use: Effective against bacteria, wild yeasts and mould even at low temperatures, so used for the cold sterilization of beverages. Shortly after performing its preservative function it breaks down into minute inactive constituents so leaves no worrying residue.
Likely products: Soft drinks; non-alcoholic wines; carbonated and non-carbonated juice beverages such as Blackcurrant Fruit Shoots; ready-to-drink teas; vitamin-enriched drinks; isotonic sport drinks; nutraceutical beverages and juice concentrates and flavoured waters.
Should you be scared of it? No.
ADI (Acceptable Daily Intake): None allocated.

E249 🍎
Potassium nitrite (Preservative)
A naturally occurring mineral.

Use: Potent against *Clostridium botulinum* (the bacteria that causes botulism), but very little used in food. Where nitrites are traditionally used, sodium nitrite is mostly favoured.
Likely products: Cured meat and fish products.
Food scares: A very strong oxidizer, so contact, inhalation and ingestion in quantity should be avoided. In high concentrations it may react with the haemoglobin in the blood so it is not allowed in products intended for children younger than 1 year as they have a different type of haemoglobin that is much more reactive to nitrites. Nitrites can also

form carcinogenic nitrosamines in the body, although several US studies have failed to establish beyond doubt that they can cause cancer at the levels to which humans are exposed to them as food additives. Nevertheless, the food industries involved have largely moved away from the use of nitrites.

Nutritional/medical benefits: Protects food against botulism, the most potent toxin on the planet.

Should you be scared of it? Possibly, as discussed above.

ADI (Acceptable Daily Intake): 0–0.6 mg/kg body weight.

E250 ◦

Sodium nitrite (Preservative)

A naturally occurring mineral.

Use: Potent against *Clostridium botulinum* (the bacteria that causes botulism), it is used both to kill this off and to colour meat and fish

Likely products: Bacon, hams and other traditional cured meat products; hot dogs, luncheon meats, corned beef and canned meatloaf. Also found in some cured fish.

Food scares: As E249, plus it has been linked to triggering migraine headaches in those susceptible to them.

Nutritional/medical benefits: Protects food against botulism, the most potent toxin on the planet. Used to dilate blood vessels and to treat sickle cell anaemia, cyanide poisoning, heart attacks, brain aneurysms, plus pulmonary hypertension in infants.

Should you be scared of it? Possibly, see E249 and above.

ADI (Acceptable Daily Intake): 0–0.6 mg/kg body weight.

E251 ◦

Sodium nitrate (Preservative)

A naturally occurring mineral known as Chile saltpetre.

Use: The nitrates have been used as preservatives for at least 2,000 years, often in combination with the nitrites and salt. They also help prevent the natural colours in food from fading.

Source: Also present in nearly all vegetables.

Natural version: Vegetables as above.

Likely products: Salami and other meat products such as sausages, bacon and hams; cheeses; pizzas and pickled herrings.

Food scares: Nitrates have no known side effects, but they do convert to nitrites when heated or in the stomach (see E249).

Nutritional/medical benefits: Protects food against botulism, the most potent toxin on the planet.

Should you be scared of it? No, but see above.

ADI (Acceptable Daily Intake): 0–3.7 mg/kg body weight.

E252 &

Potassium nitrate; Saltpetre (Preservative)

Another naturally occurring mineral commonly called saltpetre.

Use: Most commonly used as an agricultural fertilizer, it has also been widely used as a meat preservative since the Middle Ages. Because of rather unreliable results, its use in food has largely been supplanted by the use of other nitrates and nitrites.

Source: This was at one time made by composting manure with wood ashes, earth or straw but is now mostly made from ammonia.

Likely products: It is still used in French charcuterie and in the brine used to make corned beef, and even then it is used with sodium nitrate and nitrite to improve their colour.

Food scares: As E251.

Nutritional/medical benefits: Protects us against botulism, the most potent toxin on the planet. Folklore credits it with the power to decrease sex drive, but sadly there is no evidence that this is true. It is used in toothpastes for sensitive teeth.

Should you be scared of it? No, but see E251.

ADI (Acceptable Daily Intake): 0–3.7 mg/kg body weight.

E260 🍎
Acetic acid (Preservative)

A natural preservative used for thousands of years to preserve foods in pickles, acetic acid was originally made from the bacterial oxidation of alcohols such as wine, sherry, cider, etc. Nowadays the acid used as an additive is made from ethanol or hydrocarbons.

Use: As it lowers pH, it makes an excellent preservative. It may be used in conjunction with salt to inhibit yeasts, bacteria and moulds by reducing the availability of water.

Natural version: Vinegars of all types are essentially solutions of 5–10% acetic acid in water.

Likely products: Vinaigrettes and salad dressings, marinades, mayonnaise, sauces, pickling liquids, and savoury snacks such as Chicken and Mushroom Pot Noodle.

Nutritional/medical benefits: Vinegar, especially cider vinegar, is claimed to have a wide range of medical benefits, but few studies have confirmed this. Acetic acid is used for treating the sting of the box jellyfish by disabling the stinging cells, preventing serious injury or death if applied immediately, as well as for treating outer ear infections. There is some evidence that adding vinegar (or lemon juice, as also acidic) lowers the glycaemic index (GI) of a meal so may help with diabetes management and weight control in those using GI to help.

Should you be scared of it? No.

ADI (Acceptable Daily Intake): Unlimited.

E261 🍎
Potassium acetate (Acidity regulator, flavour regulator)

A synthetic compound made from acetic acid. Interestingly, it is used in the mummification of bodies (Lenin's body is one such example) and in class K fire extinguishers.

Use: To act as a preservative and to help regulate acidity in products. It is also used to modify the flavour of products that have been acidified with acetic acid (vinegar).

Likely products: None known.

Nutritional/medical benefits: Used in the treatment of diabetic ketoacidosis, a potentially life-threatening complication in people with diabetes.

Should you be scared of it? No (not unless you get hit with a fire extinguisher!)

ADI (Acceptable Daily Intake): Unlimited.

E262 🍎
Sodium acetate and sodium diacetate (Acidity regulator, buffer, flavouring)

The sodium salts of acetic acid, these are synthetic crystalline compounds.

Use: To regulate acidity and act as a buffer (keeping pH values steady), to modify the strong taste of acetic acid (vinegar), in bread production to help prevent mould. Sodium diacetate is used to give a vinegar flavour to dry foods.

Likely products: Breads, salt-and-vinegar-flavoured savoury snacks and instant soups.

Nutritional/medical benefits: None known.

Should you be scared of it? No.

ADI: (Acceptable Daily Intake): Unlimited.

E263 🍎
Calcium acetate (Acidity regulator, flavour modifier)

A synthetic compound made from acetic acid.

Use: As an acidity regulator and to fortify products with calcium. It is also used to modify the strong flavour of acetic acid (vinegar) in foods, to control mould in bread flour, and in vegetarian 'gelatine' (alginates).

Likely products: Bread, vegetarian jellies and gelling agents.

Nutritional/medical benefits: Used to prevent blood phosphate levels increasing in those with kidney disease.

Should you be scared of it? No.

ADI (Acceptable Daily Intake): Unlimited.

E270 🍎 🚶

Lactic acid (Preservative, buffer, flavour regulator)

A natural compound produced by the fermentation of beet or cane sugar, or glucose. It can also be produced synthetically.

Use: Widely used as a preservative due to its acidic properties, which prevents spoilage due to bacteria and food-borne pathogens. It is also used in combination with acetic acid to inhibit the growth of yeasts, and as a pH regulator. Its mild flavour means it is used as an acid where other acids would taste too strong. In confectionery it prevents the degradation of sugars, therefore lengthening shelf life.

Natural version: Natural lactic acid is made from the fermentation of sugar beet or cane or glucose.

Likely products: Widely used as a flavouring for foods where a cheese, cream, yoghurt or meat flavour is needed. Found in other dairy products, such as fat spreads; ricotta, feta and other brined cheeses; processed cheese; pickles; olives; low-fat mayonnaise and cooking sauces; confectionery and sour dough breads.

Food Scares: It does *not* need to be avoided by those with lactose-intolerance. In fact, as lactic acid bacteria actively convert lactose into lactic acid, ingestion of certain active strains may help lactose-intolerant individuals tolerate more lactose than they would have otherwise.

Should you be scared of it? No.

ADI (Acceptable Daily Intake): Unlimited, except in infant foods, where it is not permitted.

E280 🍎 🚶

Propionic acid (Preservative)

A naturally occurring fatty acid found in the processing of sugar and later identified as a normal constituent of bodily fluids.

Use: Inhibits the growth of moulds, fungi and some bacteria.

Source: Largely now made by chemical treatment of the gas ethylene.

Natural version: Present naturally in small quantities in many foods and in greater quantities in fermented foods such as some cheeses. Also present in animal and human sweat.

Likely products: Yeast and chemically leavened bakery products, prepacked and part-baked bread; cheeses such as Jarlsberg and cheese products; pie fillings; tomato purée; canned frankfurters and other processed meat; artificially sweetened jams, jellies and preserves.

Food scares: It is thought by some to be linked with the occurrence of migraine headaches.

Should you be scared of it? No, but see above.

ADI (Acceptable Daily Intake): Unlimited.

E281 🍎
Sodium propionate (Preservative)
The naturally occurring sodium salt of propionic acid (see E280).

Use: As E280.
Source: As E280.
Natural version: As E280.
Likely products: Baked goods, especially when chemically leavened and those using chocolate.
Food scares: As E280.
Should you be scared of it? No, but see E280.
ADI (Acceptable Daily Intake): Unlimited.

E282 🍎
Calcium propionate (Preservative)
The naturally occurring calcium salt of propionic acid (see E280).

Use: As E280.
Source: As E280.
Natural version: As E280.
Likely products: Baked goods, especially when chemically leavened and those using chocolate; some dairy products.
Food scares: As E280.
Should you be scared of it? No, but see E280.
ADI (Acceptable Daily Intake): Unlimited.

E283 🍎
Potassium propionate (Preservative)

The naturally occurring potassium salt of propionic acid (see E280).

Use: As E280.
Source: As E280.
Natural version: As E280.
Likely products: As E282.
Food scares: As E280.
Should you be scared of it? No, but see E280.
ADI (Acceptable Daily Intake): Unlimited.

E284
Boric acid (Preservative)

A compound made from the natural mineral borax, which has been used as a preservative, antiseptic and common household disinfectant for centuries.

Use: Effective against yeasts and, to a much lesser extent, moulds and bacteria. Also used as a buffer to control the acidity of foods.
Likely products: Only permitted for use in caviar.
Food scares: Considered poisonous if taken internally or inhaled in all but very small quantities, really only of concern in long-term exposure. However, a EU directive specifically mentions its possible lowering effect on fertility and that it may harm the unborn foetus.
Nutritional/medical benefits: Used to treat fungal infections and to prevent athlete's foot.
Should you be scared of it? No (unless you eat an *awful* lot of caviar), but note the above carefully.
ADI (Acceptable Daily Intake): Not allocated.

E285

Sodium tetraborate; Borax (Preservative)

Sodium salt of boric acid.

Use: Although its use is generally limited to caviar in the West, as for E285, it is still widely used in Oriental cooking for the rubbery texture it imparts to food, particularly noodles, although such use is banned by some Asian countries.

Likely products: As E284.

Food scares: Much as E284.

Nutritional/medical benefits: Used in the vaccine Gardasil.

Should you be scared of it? No (unless you eat an *awful* lot of caviar), but note the above carefully.

ADI (Acceptable Daily Intake): Not allocated.

E290 🍎

Carbon dioxide (Preservative, buffer, refrigerant)

The natural gas present in the atmosphere (one of the 'greenhouse gases') and used and produced in the respiration of plants and animals. The commercial gas is normally obtained from industrial production flues or as a by-product of fermentation.

Use: Carbonated drinks, including soft drinks, soda water and beer, chilled versions of it as dry ice. One of its most common uses is in food packaging, where it replaces air and forms a mild acid on the surface of the food that deters bacteria and moulds.

Likely products: Beers and fizzy drinks, in the packaging of products such as par-baked bread and hard cheeses, as well as poultry and fish for bulk transport. Some sweets, such as Pop Rocks, to produce popping noises when sucked.

Should you be scared of it? No.

ADI (Acceptable Daily Intake): None specified.

E296 🍎
Malic acid (Acidifier)

A natural fruit acid to be found in apples, peaches and cherries, although it is a synthetic version that is mostly used as a food additive.

Use: In food and drink products for a mild acidic flavour.
Source: Made from maleic anhydride though it occurs naturally in many fruits especially apples, peaches and cherries.
Natural version: Found in apples, cherries and other fruits, such as peaches.
Likely products: Boiled sweets and chewing gum; jams and sweet-and-sour sauces; peeled potatoes; salt-and-vinegar potato crisps and snacks such as Nik Naks Nice 'n' Spicy flavour; sports drinks, fruit drinks and fruit sorbets.
Should you be scared of it? No.
ADI (Acceptable Daily Intake): Unlimited, except for young children.

E297 🍎 👤
Fumaric acid (Flavouring agent, acidity regulator)

Although a natural compound found in many plants, including lichen and Boletus mushrooms, the type used as an additive is made chemically.

Use: Fumaric acid is used in foods as an acidity regulator and to provide a sourish acidic flavour. Because it doesn't dissolve readily in water, it is used in powdered foodstuffs.
Likely products: Powdered dessert mixes; instant tea and herb drinks; fillings and toppings for baked goods; baking powder; confectionery, chewing gum and some wines.
Food scares: None known.
Nutritional/ medical benefits: Some clinical trials have shown that fumaric acid compounds may help alleviate psoriasis.
Should you be scared of it? No.
ADI (Acceptable Daily Intake): 0–6mg/kg body weight.

E300 🍎
Ascorbic acid (Antioxidant)

An extremely common additive that's better known to the layperson as vitamin C. It's a sugar acid that occurs naturally in most fruit and vegetables, especially berries and citrus fruit, although this is an expensive source so when used as an additive, it's usually made chemically from glucose.

Use: To prevent oxidation reactions within foodstuffs, thus extending their shelf life and maintaining colour and flavour. In bread it is used to help in the formation of gluten structure and thus increase volume.

Natural version: Rose hips, fruit (especially blackcurrants) and vegetables, notably red peppers.

Likely products: Beers, wine and a wide range of foods, including bread, meat products such as canned meatloaf, some dairy products, fruit pulps, juices and drinks, and canned and dried vegetables.

Nutritional/medical benefits: It is essential for human life: without it, we would die, and as our bodies don't synthesize this, we must get it from food. It's a vital component of collagen, which is effectively the glue that holds us together, and it has long been used to treat scurvy. It has a huge range of medical benefits – it is a potent antioxidant and high doses may help protect against lead-induced nerve and muscle abnormalities, especially in smokers. It may also help promote recovery from strokes.

Should you be scared of it? No.

ADI (Acceptable Daily Intake): Unlimited.

E301 🍎

Sodium ascorbate (Antioxidant)

The sodium salt of ascorbic acid (which simply means that a molecule of this includes a sodium molecule that ascorbic acid lacks), it is still a form of vitamin C, but E301 has a higher bioavailability, so that the body can take up this essential nutrient more effectively. See E300.

Use: As E300.

Likely products: As E300, plus pork pies; sausages; Scotch eggs; Peperami; frozen fish and shellfish.

Nutritional/medical benefits: As E300, plus it can reverse the development of atherosclerotic (artery hardening) disease, helps in heart attack prevention, is used in the treatment of chronic and acute infections and to treat melanoma (skin cancer).

Should you be scared of it? No.

ADI (Acceptable Daily Intake): Unlimited.

E302 🍎 🚹

Calcium ascorbate (Antioxidant)

The calcium salt of ascorbic acid. See E300.

Use: As E300.

Natural version: As E300.

Likely products: As E300, plus canned bouillons, consommés and stocks, and Scotch eggs. Used on post-harvested and peeled or cut fruit.

Food scares: There is a concern about the calcium content contributing to kidney stones, but this is only a problem if large doses of it are taken regularly as a supplement.

Nutritional/medical benefits: Easier to digest than the other ascorbates and a good source of calcium.

Should you be scared of it? No, but see above.

ADI (Acceptable Daily Intake): None allocated.

E304 🍎 👤
Fatty acid esters of ascorbic acid (Antioxidant)

These are two synthetic fatty acids, ascorbyl palmitate and ascorbyl stearate made from ascorbic acid.

Use: They are used to allow the antioxidant effect of ascorbic acid to be used in fats and oils to prevent them form becoming rancid. Often used in conjunction with the food colours E160 and E161 to prevent them from being oxidized.

Likely products: Fats and oils, margarines and fat spreads; chicken stock cubes; pork pies and Scotch eggs; baby formula and tinned baby food.

Nutritional/medical benefits: As E300.

Should you be scared of it? No.

ADI (Acceptable Daily Intake): 0–1.25 mg/kg body weight.

E306
Tocopherols (Antioxidant)

This clear yellow oily liquid antioxidant extracted from vegetable sources, can consist of one of eight similar natural chemical compounds, known collectively as natural vitamin E. The vitamin can be one of four types of tocopherol, alpha-, beta-, gamma- and delta-tocopherol, as well as four types of related tocotrienols, d-alpha-, d-beta-, d-gamma- and d-delta-tocotrienol. Synthetic versions are also made, but these generally consist of mixtures of all eight compounds and are much less beneficial in human health and nutrition.

Use: Added to fats and oils to delay or prevent them becoming rancid.

Source: Oils from soya beans, sunflower seeds and other nuts and grains.

Natural version: Vegetables, nut, seeds and whole grains.

Likely products: Mostly margarine and low-fat spreads, vegetable oils and meat pies.

Food scares: As tocopherols are anti-coagulants, use of high-dosage supplements can cause internal bleeding and is not recommended.

Nutritional/medical benefits: Tocopherols continue to be potent antioxidants after consumption, combatting free radicals in the body. Vitamin E, in conjunction with other antioxidants such as vitamin C or zinc, has been shown to protect against age-related macular degeneration, the primary cause of blindness in older people, and glaucomatous damage. Some evidence has also been seen of tocopherols reducing the risk of heart attacks, thrombosis and Alzheimer's disease, but research continues on these claims. Vitamin E is often used in skin creams and lotions because it is believed to help encourage skin healing and reducing scarring.

Should you be scared of it? No.

ADI (Acceptable Daily Intake): 0–2 mg/kg body weight.

E307

Alpha-tocopherol (Antioxidant)

Alpha-tocopherol is very similar to E306 Tocopherol, but it is vitamin E has higher bioavailability (the body can use this version of the essential nutrient more effectively). Synthetic d-alpha-tocopherol is the most active and potent form of the vitamin.

Use: As E306.

Source: As E306.

Natural version: As E306.

Likely products: Animal fats and vegetable oils, cheeses, pork products, soups.

Food scares: As E306.

Nutritional/medical benefits: As E306.

Should you be scared of it? No.

ADI (Acceptable Daily Intake): 0.15–2 mg/kg body weight.

E308

Gamma-tocopherol (Antioxidant)

Gamma-tocopherol is a form of vitamin E with rather low vitamin activity but stronger antioxidant properties in food.

Use: As E306.

Source: As E306.

Natural version: As E306.
Likely products: Animal fats and vegetable oils, mainly olive oil.
Food scares: As E306.
Nutritional/medical benefits: As E306.
Should you be scared of it? No.
ADI (Acceptable Daily Intake): 0.15–2 mg/kg body weight.

E309
Delta-tocopherol (Antioxidant)

Delta-tocopherol is a form of vitamin E with rather low vitamin activity but the strongest antioxidant properties in food, roughly, twice that of gamma (E308) and three or four times that of alpha (E306).

Use: As E306.
Source: As E306.
Natural version: As E306.
Likely products: As E306.
Food scares: As E306.
Nutritional/medical benefits: As E306.
Should you be scared of it? No.
ADI (Acceptable Daily Intake): 0.15–2 mg/kg body weight.

E310
Propyl gallate (Antioxidant)

A synthetic fat-soluble antioxidant, although a natural version is also made from the pods of the Tara tree (*Caesalpinea spinosa*).

Use: To prevent or delay fats, particularly polyunsaturated fats, going rancid. It is often used together with E320 and E321 for best antioxidant effect.
Likely products: Polyunsaturated oils, margarine and salad dressings; meat products, microwaveable popcorn, soup mixes, chewing gum and frozen meals.
Food scares: It breaks down in the stomach to produce gallic acid which,

in high enough doses, could cause eczema, stomach, kidney and liver problems, and hyperactivity. Recent studies also indicate an effect on estrogen in women. The maximum daily intake is kept deliberately low to avoid this.

Nutritional/medical benefits: The gallates exhibit non-antibiotic antibacterial properties.

Should you be scared of it? No, not at permitted levels, but note the above.

ADI (Acceptable Daily Intake): 0–1.4 mg/kg body weight.

E311
Octyl gallate (Antioxidant)
A synthetic fat-soluble antioxidant and preservative.

Use: As E310.
Likely products: As E310.
Food scares: As E310.
Nutritional/medical benefits: As E310.
Should you be scared of it? No, but see E310.
ADI (Acceptable Daily Intake): Not allocated.

E312
Dodecyl gallate (Antioxidant)
A synthetic fat-soluble antioxidant.

Use: As E310.
Likely products: As E310.
Food scares: As E310.
Nutritional/medical benefits: See E310. Dodecyl gallate is particularly effective against antibiotic-resistant MRSA.
Should you be scared of it? As E310.
ADI (Acceptable Daily Intake): Not allocated.

E315
Erythorbic acid (Antioxidant)

A synthetic version of ascorbic acid (E300, vitamin C) produced from sucrose.

Use: It has little vitamin function but displays the same antioxidant powers as the ascorbates, so is widely used in preference as it is cheaper.
Likely products: Preserved and cured meat products and preserved and semi-preserved fish products.
Should you be scared of it? No.
ADI (Acceptable Daily Intake): None specified.

E316
Sodium erythorbate (Antioxidant)

The sodium salt of erythorbic acid and a synthetic version of sodium ascorbate (E301, a sodium salt of vitamin C).

Use: As E315.
Likely products: As E315.
Food scares: As E315.
Should you be scared of it? No.
ADI (Acceptable Daily Intake): None specified.

E319
Tertiary-butyl hydroquinone (TBHQ); Butylhydroxinon (Antioxidant)

A synthetic organic phenol (phenol is an antiseptic carbolic acid that looks like white or pink-tinged powder). 'Synthetic organic' may sound like a contradiction in terms, but 'organic' just means that the compound contains carbon.

Use: This antioxidant is particularly effective in stabilizing highly unsaturated oils and preventing fried food products against oxidation.
Likely products: Vegetable oils used in the manufacture of heat-treated

foods, especially potato crisps and chips, dried cereals and meats.

Food scares: Some studies have shown a link between prolonged high doses and cancers, while other studies would seem to have detected an anti-cancer effect. This is a classic example of dramatic toxicology: it has extremely beneficial potential (it's a potent antiseptic and helps make keep food from going off), yet it also has extremely toxic potential, and can cause death by injection. Fear not: its use is tightly controlled.

Should you be scared of it? No.

ADI (Acceptable Daily Intake): 0–0.7 mg/kg body weight.

E320
Butylated hydroxyanisole (BHA)(Antioxidant)

A synthetic antioxidant made from petroleum.

Use: An antioxidant used to prevent or delay fats and oils from becoming rancid. It is often used in tandem with E321 (BHT).

Likely products: Frying oils; animal fats; butter; meats; cereals; dried potatoes; baked and fried foods and beer.

Food scares: Both BHA and E311 (BHT) have been blamed for major problems as there's evidence that at high doses they may contribute to carcinogenicity in rats and mice; however the same reactions may combat oxidative stress. There is evidence that certain persons may have difficulty metabolizing BHA and BHT, resulting in health and behaviour changes.

Nutritional/medical benefits: BHA and E311 (BHT) may have antiviral and antimicrobial effects.

Should you be scared of it? No, but note the above.

ADI (Acceptable Daily Intake): 0–0.5 mg/kg body weight.

E321
Butylated hydroxytoluene (BHT)(Antioxidant)
A synthetic antioxidant.

Use: As E320.
Likely products: Fats and oils; baked products.
Food scares: As E320.
Nutritional/medical benefits: As E320. Research is underway concerning the use of BHT in the treatment of herpes simplex and AIDS.
Should you be scared of it? No, but note the above.
ADI (Acceptable Daily Intake): 0–0.5 mg/kg body weight.

E322 ꙮ
Lecithins (Emulsifier)
These are fatty substances found in animal and plant tissue, and in egg yolks.

Use: Apart from their natural nutritive value, their action of lowering the surface tension of water means these are used as emulsifiers and stabilizers of foods that consist of oil-in-water or water-in-oil emulsions. They are also used to help powdered instant foods dissolve in water and to assist the development of gluten in baked goods, as well as in high-fat margarines to prevent spattering when they are used for cooking.
Source: Soya bean oil, sunflower oil and eggs.
Natural version: As above.
Likely products: Margarines; dressings; chocolate and confectionery, such as M&Ms; instant sauce/soup/etc powders; McCain Micro Cheese and Tomato Pizzas and baked goods.
Nutritional/medical benefits: Some studies indicate that soy lecithins help lower bad cholesterol and triglycerides in the blood while in increasing the good cholesterol. There is also a line of study on the idea that lecithins could help Alzheimer's Disease sufferers.
Should you be scared of it? No.
ADI (Acceptable Daily Intake): Unlimited.

E325 🍎 🕴

Sodium lactate

E326 🍎

Potassium lactate (Preservatives, buffers, flavourings)

Although both are available naturally, for use as additives these salts of lactic acid are made synthetically from the acid.

Use: To extend shelf life and increase food safety as they have broad antimicrobial actions and are effective at inhibiting most spoilage and pathogenic bacteria. Also as mildly sharp flavourings, and helping to regulate the pH of products.

Likely products: Fresh meat products, sausages, ham, poultry products, deli items, roast beef, cooking sauces and ready meals and confectionery.

Nutritional/medical benefits: Sodium lactate is commonly used to treat certain types of arrhythmias (irregular heart beat).

Should you be scared of them? No.

ADI (Acceptable Daily Intake): Unlimited, in fact both can be widely used as it they are classified as GRAS (generally recognized as safe) in the USA.

E327 🍎

Calcium lactate (Mineral supplement, texturizer, coagulant)

A compound commonly used as a source of calcium, it is available both naturally and by the chemical treatment of lactic acid.

Use: Highly bio-available and easily metabolized, it is valued as a source of calcium. It is added to freshly cut fruits such as melon to keep them firm and can also improve the texture of fruit pastes due to its effect on pectin, and its coagulation of proteins.

Likely products: Soft drinks; fresh fruit; fruit juices and pastes; canned fruit; milk; infant foods and diet foods (for fortification purposes) and pickles.

Nutritional/medical benefits: Easily absorbed, so used in supplements.

It is added to sugar-free foods to help prevent tooth decay and, when add to chewing gums containing xylitol, it remineralizes tooth enamel. It is also an effective antacid.

Should you be scared of it? No.

ADI (Acceptable Daily Intake): Unlimited.

||||||||||||||||||||||||||||||||||||||||||||||||||||||||||||||||||||||||||||||||||||||||||||||||||||||||||||||||||||||||||||||||||||||||||||||||||||||

E330 🍎 🧍
Citric acid (Preservative, flavouring, antioxidant)

An extremely common natural E, this is a weak organic acid with a bewildering array of uses, and without which a lot of our food would be more expensive, duller-tasting and shorter-lasting. I use it for jellies and to give tartness and a longer life to my legendary elderflower cordial. Around 1.7m tonnes are produced annually. Widely used in foods, it is found in many fruits, notably citrus fruits and is commercially made by fermenting molasses with strains of the fungus *Aspergillus niger*.

Use: A huge variety of uses: the main ones are as a flavouring to add a clean tart taste to foods and drinks; an antioxidant to stop discoloration and/or decomposition, especially in fruits; helps jam to set; helps bread to rise and stops fats going rancid (off).

Natural version: Sour citrus fruits such as lemons and limes contain lots of naturally occurring citric acid. When you use a squeeze of lemon to stop slices of fruit or vegetables going brown, you're using it as an antioxidant.

Likely products: Jams, jellies and preserves; ice creams; soups and sauces; as a ripening agent in the making of cheeses such as mozzarella; frozen fish; bread; soft drinks including carbonated drinks; fruit nectars; juices and squashes and sweets (think lemon sherbets); infant food and wines.

Food scares: In large quantities it can cause erosion of teeth and there are extremely rare reports of Citric Acid Intolerance, although this would apply to lemons as much as E330.

Nutritional/medical benefits: The body uses it in the process of turning food into energy (the Krebs cycle).

Should you be scared of it? No, but be sensible when handling it in pure form, as it is an acid and could cause skin irritation.

ADI (Acceptable Daily Intake): Unlimited.

E331 🍎 👤

Sodium citrates (Acidity regulators, antioxidants, emulsifiers)

This additive name covers 3 citrates based on sodium, monosodium, disodium and trisodium citrate. These citrates are all widely found in nature but are mostly produced commercially from citric acid. Trisodium citrate is the one most often used as an additive.

Use: As acidity regulators in soft drinks, desserts, jams and sweets, and as emulsifiers in processed cheese and meats.

Likely products: Jams and preserves; desserts and baked goods; processed cheeses and meats; soft drinks and confectionery.

Nutritional/medical benefits: Some studies seem to have shown that sodium citrate helps performance runners but the evidence is not conclusive.

Should you be scared of it? No.

ADI (Acceptable Daily Intake): Unlimited.

E332 🍎 👤

Potassium citrates (Acidity regulator, mineral supplement)

As with the previous citrates (E331), these are widely found in nature but again, are mostly produced commercially from citric acid.

Use: As acidity regulators and as sources of potassium.

Likely products: Beverages, especially soft drinks, and confectionery.

Nutritional/medical benefits: These are used medicinally to treat kidney stones as they neutralize the acid in urine. For the same reason, they are also used as non-irritating diuretics and to treat some urinary problems and gout. However there are contraindications, so they should only be used on the advice of a GP. They can be used as dietary supplements, but care is needed, and fruit and vegetables are a great source of dietary potassium that you should use as a first resort.

Should you be scared of it? Not as food additives, but exercise caution if you are self-administering them as supplements.

ADI (Acceptable Daily Intake): Unlimited.

E333 🍎
Calcium citrates: Monocalcium citrate; Dicalcium citrate; Tricalcium citrate (Preservatives, acidity regulators, mineral sources, gelling agents, flavour modifiers)

Citrates, the salts of citric acid (E330), are found widely in nature. Tricalcium citrate is the type most commonly produced commercially as an additive.

Use: Calcium citrates are used mostly as acidity regulators and as sources of calcium. The citrates also help form acid-based gels, such as with alginates and pectin, and moderate the flavour of acidic drinks.
Likely products: Nutritional and dietary supplements in beverages; desserts; baby foods and processed vegetables.
Should you be scared of it? No.
ADI (Acceptable Daily Intake): Unlimited.

E334 🍎
L (+) Tartaric acid (Flavouring, raising agent, chelator, antioxidant)

Most of the tartaric acid used in commerce is made from potassium tartrate produced as a by-product of the fermentation of grape juice into wine. It is also synthesized chemically from maleic acid.

Use: To provide a distinctly acid flavour in foods, especially those where a sour acid rather than fresh acid flavour are wanted. It is also a component of baking powder where it releases CO_2.
Source: It is synthetically made from maleic acid.
Likely products: Most commonly found in baking powder, but also used in jam and biscuits, and sour-flavoured confectionery.
Should you be scared of it? In very large doses it is thought to cause muscle paralysis, but this would mean consuming more than half a kilo of the pure form.
ADI (Acceptable Daily Intake): 0–0.3mg/kg bodyweight.

E335 🍎
Sodium tartrates: Monosodium tartrate; Disodium tartrate

E336 🍎
Potassium tartrates: Monopotassium tartrate; Cream of tartar; Dipotassium tartrate

E337 🍎
Sodium potassium tartrate; Rochelle salt (Flavour modifiers, acidity regulators, emulsifiers, antioxidants, buffers)

Monopotassium tartrate is a natural compound made as a by-product of the fermentation of grape juice. This is then used to make the dipotassium salt by chemical means. The sodium tartrates are made from commercial tartaric acid. Sodium potassium tartrate is sometimes called 'wine diamonds' in wine as it is the crystalline product found on the cork. It is used for silvering mirrors and experiments on crystal growing on board Skylab.

Use: These tartrates are all used to help adjust the taste of products that contain tartaric acid. Monopotassium tartrate (cream of tartar) is found in baking powders as a source of acidity to produce the release of carbon dioxide. Dipotassium tartrate is used to stabilize egg whites, increasing their heat tolerance and volume, and preventing sugar syrups from crystallizing. Sodium tartrates are used as emulsifiers and binding agents in products such as jellies, margarine and sausage casings.

Likely products: Baking powders; sugar syrups; jellies; margarine; sausages and products containing egg whites.

Nutritional/medical benefits: Sodium potassium tartrate is used as a laxative.

Should you be scared of them? No.

ADI (Acceptable Daily Intake): None set.

E338
Phosphoric acid (Acidulant, setting agent, flavour modifier, buffer)

A synthetic compound made from phosphate-rich rock.

Use: A strong food-grade acid, it is cheap to produce and therefore widely used, especially in soft drinks, particularly colas, in which it is valued for its strong acid flavour and for increasing the acidity of the drink, which also helps (along with preservatives) to delay spoilage by microorganisms. It is also used in the refining of sugar.

Likely products: Beer, soft drinks especially colas such as Coca-Cola (where it is listed as phosphoric acid), sugar, jam and cheese.

Food scares: None, though some evidence suggests that consumption of phosphoric acid-containing soft drinks is associated with low bone density (which can lead to osteoporosis). This has not been convincingly established and is disputed in other studies.

Nutritional/medical benefits: Dentists use it to whiten teeth.

Should you be scared of it? No, but consumption of very large quantities of any soft drink could potentially lead to problems.

ADI (Acceptable Daily Intake): The maximum tolerable daily intake is set at 70mg/kg bodyweight.

E339
Sodium phosphates: Monosodium phosphate; Disodium phosphate; Trisodium phosphate

E340
Potassium phosphates: Monopotassium phosphate; Dipotassium phosphate; Tripotassium phosphate (Acidulants, chelating agents, buffers, emulsifiers)

The two sets of phosphates are virtually interchangeable in their properties although the disodium and dipotassium phosphates are those most commonly used in foods.

Use: Monosodium and monopotassium phosphates are acidic and are therefore used in raising agents. The disodium and dipotassium phosphates are mostly used to enhance water binding in meat and dairy produce to prevent shrinkage during cooking and storage, as well as stabilizing milk products and conversely encouraging gelling in things like instant puddings and cheesecakes. They prevent clumping in milk-based powder so dried milk dissolves more easily. In processed cheese they help emulsification enabling the cheese to be melted without the fat separating out. Trisodium phosphate is mostly used as a buffer and to improve the texture of meat and cheese.

Likely products: Cheeses and processed cheese; ready-meals; tinned food;cooked hams and other meats; milk and dairy products; evaporated and powdered milk; desserts and baked goods.

Should you be scared of them? No.

ADI (Acceptable Daily Intake): The maximum tolerable daily intake is set at 70 mg/kg bodyweight.

E341 🍎

Calcium phosphates: Monocalcium phosphate; Dicalcium phosphate; Tricalcium phosphate (Raising agents, free-flow agent)

Synthetic compounds made from phosphoric acid treated with hydrated lime. Tooth enamel is also largely calcium phosphate.

Use: Monocalcium phosphate is used as a raising agent and also as a bread enhancer in low-gluten flours in which it also prevents bacterial spoilage. Dicalcium phosphate is also used as a raising agent, particularly suited to long baking. Tricalcium phosphate is mainly used as a free-flow agent in powders to avoid formation of clumps.

Likely products: Monocalcium phosphate: canned fruit, milk desserts and powdered drinks.

Dicalcium phosphate: cakes.

Tricalcium phosphate: powdered drinks, soups and sauces.

Should you be scared of them? No.

ADI (Acceptable Daily Intake): The maximum tolerable daily intake is set at up to 70 mg/kg body weight.

E343
Magnesium phosphates: Monomagnesium phosphate; Dimagnesium phosphate; Trimagnesium phosphate (Acidulants, stabilizers)

The synthetically made magnesium salts of phosphoric acid.

Use: As an acidulant in baking powder and as a source of magnesium in food supplements. Used as stabilizers in baked goods, especially cakes where there is a delay from production to baking, as they react slowly.

Source: Synthetically made from chemical reaction of two other additives E530 and E338.

Likely products: Baking powder and cakes. Food supplements.

Nutritional/medical benefits: Used as antacids and laxatives.

Should you be scared of them? No.

ADI (Acceptable Daily Intake): The maximum tolerable daily intake is set at 70mg/kg bodyweight.

E350
Sodium malates: Sodium malate; Sodium hydrogen malate

E351
Potassium malate

E352
Calcium malates: Calcium malate; Calcium hydrogen malate (Acidity regulators, buffers, flavour modifiers, antioxidants)

Synthetic compounds made from malic acid (E296).

Use: Malates are mostly used to buffer and modify the strong acid taste of foods that contain malic acid. They are therefore generally used to complement the flavours of products containing apples, often in soft drinks and confectionery.

Likely products: Jams and apple- or fruit-flavoured soft drinks and confectionery; canned vegetables; soups and sauces.
Should you be scared of them? No.
ADI (Acceptable Daily Intake): Not specified, but certain forms are not allowed in baby foods.

E353
Metatartaric acid; Glucaric acid (Acidity regulator, emulsifier)

Synthetic compound made from glucose.

Use: This is only found in wine and some fruit juices, where it regulates acidity, and, in wine, prevents deposits forming.
Likely products: Wine.
Should you be scared of it? No.
ADI (Acceptable Daily Intake): Not specified, but limited in wine up to 100mg per litre.

E354
Calcium tartrate (Preservative, buffer)

A natural by-product of wine-making made from the dregs.

Use: Acts as a preservative and regulates acidity in foods.
Source: By-product of the fermentation of grapes.
Likely products: Fish and fruit preserves, products containing seaweed.
Should you be scared of it? No.
ADI (Acceptable Daily Intake): Not allocated.

E355
Adipic acid

E356
Sodium adipate

E357
Potassium adipate (Acidifiers, flavour modifiers, buffers, gelling agent)

Synthetic compounds, the adipates are salts of the acid and made from it. Adipic acid is used in the manufacture of nylon.

Use: Adipic acid is used to provide an acid taste in products and one that has a more lingering flavour, but is now only permitted in fillings for baked goods, dessert mixes and powdered beverages. The adipates are used to modify the taste of adipic acid in products, and their use limited to the same products.

Likely products: Fruit pies; bakery products; dessert mixes and powdered drinks.

Nutritional/medical benefits: Used externally for the treatment of rheumatism.

Should you be scared of them? No.

ADI (Acceptable Daily Intake): 0–5 mg/kg body weight.

E363
Succinic acid (Flavouring agent, acidity regulator)

Also known as spirit of amber, this occurs naturally in a wide range of vegetables, but the additive E363 is almost entirely manufactured from acetic, fumaric and maleic acids and used for its distinctive acid taste.

Use: As a flavour enhancer and acidity regulator, especially in powdered foodstuffs as it doesn't cause clumping.

Source: It can be made naturally from vinegar (acetic acid), fumaric or maleic acids.

Likely products: Powdered soups, drinks and desserts.

Should you be scared of it? No, it is metabolized in the body.

ADI (Acceptable Daily Intake): Current levels are acceptable.

E380
Triammonium citrate (Acidity regulator, chelating agent)

A synthetic compound made from citric acid and ammonium hydroxide.

Use: Little used in the food industry, its only applications are as an acidity regulator, yeast food and chelating agent.
Likely products: Little used.
Should you be scared of it? No.
ADI (Acceptable Daily Intake): Unlimited.

E385
Calcium EDTA (Preservative, sequestrant)

This can help prevent foods from going rancid and therefore lengthens shelf life. It has the ability to bind metals by swapping its calcium. It is much more widely used in medicine particularly in blood analysis and by dentists as they prepare for root canal work. EDTA stands for ethylene diamine tetraacetic acid.

Use: To increase shelf life. Also used where vitamins A, C and E are present, to prevent their destruction.
Likely products: Soft drinks, fat spreads.
Should you be scared of it? No.
ADI (Acceptable Daily Intake): 0–2.5 mg/kg bodyweight.

E400 🍎 🧍
Alginic acid (Emulsifier, thickener, stabilizer)

Alginate is the principal structural component of brown seaweeds, in the way that cellulose is for land plants, and generally those that are used as food additives are made from local brown seaweeds from all over the world.

Use: Alginate swells in water (it is capable of absorbing 200–300 times its own weight) but does not dissolve, so one of its principal uses is in medical tablets as the swelling helps the tablets disintegrate. Alginic acid in food is mainly used as a stabilizer in ice cream and whipped dairy cream. Ferran Adrià, the Spanish molecular gastronomy chef uses it to make bubbles that explode in the mouth to release fruit and vegetable juices.

Source: Various types of brown seaweeds.

Likely products: Principally ice cream and ready-whipped dairy cream.

Nutritional/medical benefits: Ingested alginic acid has been reported to be able to bind potentially toxic heavy metals, like mercury, cadmium and lead, and carry them out of the system. Separate studies have also found that it similarly removed traces of low-level radioactive material. Its swelling property means that it is often used as an appetite suppressant in those trying to lose weight.

Should you be scared of it? No.

ADI (Acceptable Daily Intake): Not specified.

E401
Sodium alginate (Emulsifier, thickener, stabilizer)

The sodium salt of alginic acid, this is extracted as a flavourless gum from brown seaweed.

Use: As a food thickener and stabilizer and in the production of gel-like foods, such as imitation pieces of fruit, like cherries, in baked goods, which are really just gelled jam. The same is true of the pimento stuffing of some olives, which is inserted into the olive as a paste and then jelled to appear to be a whole piece of pimento. The same process is also used on meat and poultry to form it into a shape or give it a chunky texture.

Source: As E400.

Natural version: As E400.

Likely products: Sauces, salad dressings, desserts, fruit pies and other products; ice creams and water ices; low-fat spreads; creams in baked goods and frozen onion rings.

Nutritional/medical benefits: As E400.

Should you be scared of it? No.

ADI (Acceptable Daily Intake): Not specified.

E402
Potassium alginate (Emulsifier, thickener, stabilizer, gelling agent)

The potassium salt of alginic acid, this is extracted as a flavourless gum from brown seaweed.

Use: As E401.
Source: As E400.
Likely products: As E401.
Nutritional/medical benefits: AS E400.
Should you be scared of it? No.
ADI (Acceptable Daily Intake): Not specified.

E403
Ammonium alginate (Emulsifier, thickener, stabilizer, gelling agent)

The ammonium salt of alginic acid, this is extracted from brown seaweed.

Use: As E401.
Source: As E400.
Likely products: As E401.
Nutritional/medical benefits: AS E400.
Should you be scared of it? No.
ADI (Acceptable Daily Intake): Not specified.

E404
Calcium alginate (Emulsifier, thickener, stabilizer, gelling agent)

The calcium salt of alginic acid, this is extracted from brown seaweed.

Use: As E401.
Source: As E400.
Likely products: As E401.
Nutritional/medical benefits: AS E400, plus used as a dressing for wounds.

Should you be scared of it? No.
ADI (Acceptable Daily Intake): Not specified.

::

E405
Propane-1,2-diol alginate; Propylene glycol alginate; Alginate ester (Emulsifier)

A cold-water soluble alginate made from alginic acid.

Use: As E401.
Source: As E400.
Likely products: Salad dressings; meringues; ice cream; noodles; fermented milk; dairy desserts and beer.
Nutritional/medical benefits: AS E400.
Should you be scared of it? No.
ADI (Acceptable Daily Intake): Not specified.

E406
Agar; Agar agar (Thickener, gelling agent)

A gelatinous substance obtained from various types of red seaweed.

Use: As a vegetarian gelatin substitute, a thickener for soups and a gelling agent in jellies and ice creams.
Source: Various types of red seaweeds.
Likely products: Jams and marmalades; toppings and fillings for baked goods; gelled meats and aspics; fermented dairy products and desserts. In Asia, agar is used in many traditional dishes, such as red bean jelly, tokoroten noodles and mitsumame.
Nutritional/medical benefits: A good source of iodine, calcium, iron, phosphorus and several vitamins.
Should you be scared of it? No.
ADI (Acceptable Daily Intake): Unlimited.

E407
Carrageenan (Thickener, gelling agent, stabilizer)

A natural substance obtained from the *Chondrus crispus* variety of red seaweed, also known as Irish or carrageenan moss, and various related species.

Use: Used for its gelling, thickening and stabilizing properties in dairy products and processed foods. It is also used as a clarifying agent in the brewing of beer.

Source: Various types of red seaweeds.

Natural version: See above.

Likely products: Dairy desserts powder mixes for the same; flavoured milk drinks; creams and toppings; ice creams, such as Ben & Jerry's Chunky Monkey flavour; meat, ham and poultry; fish products; processed cheeses; cottage cheese; sauces and dressings; glazes for baked goods.

Food scares: A small number of people seem to be sensitive to carrageenan, developing stomach pains similar to those from IBS, and possibly even ulcers. A recent review of animal studies suggested that degraded carrageenan might be associated with cancer in the gastrointestinal tract. But comparable evidence does not exist in humans.

Should you be scared of it? No, but note the above.

ADI (Acceptable Daily Intake): Not specified.

E407a
Processed eucheuma seaweed (PES)
(Thickener, gelling agent, stabilizer)

Another product obtained from red seaweed, but different varieties.

Use: As a gelling, water-binding, thickening and stabilizing agent in foods such as hams and poultry products, etc. Used much in the same ways as carrageenan and often used with it.

Source: Varieties of red seaweed.

Natural version: See above.

Likely products: Hams; rolled and shaped poultry; chocolate milk; dairy desserts and ice cream.

Food scares: See E407.

Should you be scared of it? No, but note the above.
ADI (Acceptable Daily Intake): Not specified.

E410
Locust bean gum; Carob bean gum; Carobin (Thickener, gelling agent, stabilizer)

Obtained from the seeds of the locust bean (carob) tree, *Ceratonia siliqua*, found all round the Mediterranean, this natural gum is used as a highly efficient thickener and gelling agent.

Use: As a thickener in hot-prepared fabricated foods, such as sauces and soups, usually in conjunction with xanthan (E415) and carrageenan (E407) as a gelling agent in set desserts and mousses.
Source: Locust beans.
Likely products: Ice creams, cultured dairy products, such as Bio Green Original Drinking Yoghurts, and cream cheese; soups; sauces; ketchups; mayonnaise; chestnuts in liquid; dressing and desserts.
Nutritional/medical benefits: Helps bowel functions and to lower blood cholesterol levels.
Should you be scared of it? No.
ADI (Acceptable Daily Intake): Not specified.

E412
Guar gum; Guaran (Thickener, stabilizer, emulsifier, gelling agent)

A natural gum obtained from the seeds of the guar plant, *Cyamopsis tetragonolobus*, found in north west India and Pakistan, this is used as a highly efficient thickener (with eight times the thickening power of cornflour).

Likely products: Drinks; sauces; soups; ketchup; mayonnaise; chestnuts in liquid; cold-prepared frozen foods and baked goods.
Nutritional/medical benefits: As E410.
Should you be scared of it? No.
ADI (Acceptable Daily Intake): Not specified.

E413
Tragacanth gum
(Emulsifier, thickener, stabilizer)

This is a natural gum exuded by shrubs in the *Astragalus* family, mainly *A. microcephalus* and *A. gummifer*, found in arid regions of Iran and Turkey.

Use: An extremely effective thickener giving high viscosity at low concentrations and unusual in that it both thickens and emulsifies, this can be used to stabilize food emulsions, particularly pourable ones. It also has a particularly creamy mouthfeel and little or no flavour, so makes an excellent replacement for starches in dressings, etc. It is also often used in icings as it helps make them easier to handle and spread.

Likely products: Confectionery; icing; pourable and spoonable dressings and sauces; oil emulsions; ice cream; processed cheeses; cream cheese; cottage cheese and fruit drinks.

Food scares: A small proportion of people are sensitive to it.

Nutritional/medical benefits: It contains an alkaloid that has traditionally been used as a herbal remedy for coughs and diarrhoea. As a paste it has been used as a topical treatment for burns.

Should you be scared of it? No, but note the above.

ADI (Acceptable Daily Intake): Not specified.

E414
Acacia gum; Gum arabic
(Emulsifier, thickener, stabilizer)

This is a natural gum exuded by trees of the species *Acacia Senegal* (L) Willd, which mostly grows wild but some are cultivated, mainly located in the Sudan.

Use: Colourless, odourless and tasteless, this gum imparts mouthfeel without gumminess and is particularly prized for its ability to encapsulate flavouring oils for use both in soft drinks and for spray-drying to make powdered food products.

Likely products: Soft drinks and syrups; beer; wine; instant powdered soups and sauces etc; jellies; chewing gum and sweets.

Nutritional/medical benefits: A small number of people are sensitive to it.
Should you be scared of it? No, but note the above.
ADI (Acceptable Daily Intake): Not specified.

E415
Xanthan gum (Emulsifier, stabilizer, thickener)
This is a synthetic gum made by the fermentation of sugars by the bacterium *Xanthomonas campestris*.

Use: Providing both body and mouthfeel to sauces and dressings, xanthan gum is also used in gluten-free baking to give the dough or batter a 'stickiness' that would otherwise be achieved with the gluten. In baking it is also useful in reducing splashing during the filling of moulds. Xanthan gum also helps thicken commercial egg substitutes made from egg whites, to replace the fat and emulsifiers found in yolks. In drinks, it again improves mouthfeel, particularly in diet products, and holds particles of foods like cocoa and orange pulp in suspension.

Likely products: Sauces and dressings; drinks; cakes; fruit products;desserts, meat products and chestnuts in liquid.

Food scares: The benefit mentioned below can, in some people, become too effective, producing pain and diarrhoea.

Nutritional/medical benefits: It is a very efficient laxative.

Should you be scared of it? No, but note the above.

ADI (Acceptable Daily Intake): Not specified.

E416
Karaya gum; Sterculia gum
(Thickener, emulsifier)

This is a natural gum exuded by trees of the species *Sterculia urens* (Roxburgh), other species of *Sterculia and Cochlospermum*, which mostly grow in India and west Africa.

Use: Karaya is useful as a thickener as it does not have the 'gummy' texture of other gum additives. Its rather acidic flavour does restrict its use to foods in which this will be masked or not noticed, such as strongly flavoured sauces.

Likely products: Dressings and sauces, particularly brown sauces; coatings; fillings and toppings; dairy products, especially cheese spreads, whipped cream (real and imitation) and meringue powders; meat processing and chewing gum. In combination with Carrageenan E407, Karaya retards staling of bread and doughnut mixes, and other baked goods.

Nutritional/medical benefits: An effective laxative.

Should you be scared of it? No.

ADI (Acceptable Daily Intake): Not specified.

E417
Tara gum (Thickener, gelling agent, stabilizer)

A natural gum obtained from the seeds of the Tara shrub, *Caesalpinia spinosa*, found in Peru and Ecuador

Use: An efficient thickening and gelling agent, it is primarily used as a thickener in fabricated foods.

Likely products: Soups, sauces and ketchups; dressings and mayonnaise, ice creams.

Nutritional/medical benefits: Peruvians gargle with infusions of the pods for inflamed tonsils and for washing wounds; it is also used for fevers, colds and stomachaches. Helps bowel function and to lower blood cholesterol levels.

Should you be scared of it? No.

ADI (Acceptable Daily Intake): Not specified.

E418
Gellan gum (Gelling agent, thickener, emulsifier, stabilizer)

A natural substance produced by a bacterium, *Sphingomonas elodea*.

Use: Very effective at low concentrations and does not mask the flavours in food.

Likely products: A wide range of fruit preparations, including fillings and bakery jams, aspics and jellies; confectionery; crisps and nuts and soft drinks such as Sunny Delight.

ADI (Acceptable Daily Intake): Not specified.

E420
(i) Sorbitol; Glucitol; (ii) Sorbitol syrup; Glucitol syrup (Sweetener)

This is a natural nutritive sweetener found in a wide range of fruits such as apples, prunes, cherries, grapes and berries from trees of the genus *Sorbus*, although when used as an additive it is usually made from dextrose and glucose. Its sweetening power is only 60% that of ordinary sugar.

Use: As well as being used to replace ordinary sugar and glucose in sugar-free confectionery, candies and chewing gum, sorbitol is valued for its emulsifying powers in confectionery and baked products, as well as mayonnaises, creams and sauces. Sorbitol also masks the bitter aftertaste of saccharin in drinks and helps to maintain the physical texture of chewy sweets.

Natural version: Some fruits, such as apples, prunes, cherries and grapes, and berries from trees of the genus *Sorbus*.

Likely products: Diet foods; diabetic soft drinks; ice cream; jams; pastries and cakes; raisins and sweets sugar-free confectionery; candies and chewing gum; baked products; mayonnaises; creams and sauces and fish products.

Food scares: Excessive consumption can cause bloating and flatulence, and have a laxative effect. However, a few people are intolerant to the compound and experience painful symptoms at quite low levels of ingestion. It is not allowed in foods intended specifically for babies or young children.

Nutritional/medical benefits: Useful for people who want to reduce their calorie intake and may help combat obesity, Sorbitol is converted into sugar in the bloodstream, but as it is only absorbed slowly and doesn't require insulin, it is a useful source of sugar for diabetics. It does not contribute to tooth decay or cause increase in blood glucose.

Should you be scared of it? No, but note the above.

ADI (Acceptable Daily Intake): Not specified.

E421
Mannitol; D-mannitol (Sweetener)

Like sorbitol, mannitol is widely present in nature, particularly in fruits, other plants and algae, but the form of it used as an additive is usually made from fructose or mannose. It was first obtained from the flowering ash, called 'manna' after its resemblance to the Biblical food, hence its name.

Use: It is used as a low-calorie sweetener and as an anti-caking agent. It is also often employed for its pleasant taste and mouth-feel.

Natural version: Some fruits and algae.

Likely products: Baked goods and sugar-free chewing gum and confectionery.

Food scares: Excessive consumption can cause bloating and flatulence, and have a laxative effect on those few people intolerant to it.

Nutritional/medical benefits: It does not contribute to tooth decay or cause increase in blood glucose. It is useful for people who want to reduce their calorie intake, and may help combat obesity, Sold as a laxative for children, mannitol has many important medical uses. It is used to open the blood/brain barrier to allow delivery of drugs to the brain in cases of Alzheimer's Disease, etc; to treat patients with certain forms of renal failure and to protect the kidneys of patients undergoing cardiopulmonary bypass; to treat cystic fibrosis and bronchiectasis, and in cases of animal glaucoma by vets. It has also been used recently to reduce intercranial pressure in several cases of severe head trauma, but this use is still controversial.

Should you be scared of it? No, but note the above.

ADI (Acceptable Daily Intake): Not specified.

E422 ●🏃

Glycerol; Glycerin(e) (Flavouring agent, humectant, plasticizer, preservative, sweetener)

Glycerol is a type of carbohydrate naturally present in many foods and some is even formed in the body. Commercially, it is obtained from animal and vegetable fats. It is safe and has been used for many generations. In the days before 'Australian soft icing' glycerol or glycerine was added to royal icing to prevent it from setting rock hard.

Use: It adds moisture to foods without the need for adding water, which might increase the risk of food spoilage from moulds and yeasts. It is sweet but not as sweet as table sugar and does not readily crystallize, so can be added to products where sugar crystals may form in storage. May be used as a low-calorie sweetener as it contains fewer calories per gram than table sugar.

Likely products: Cakes and baked goods, soft drinks.

Nutritional/medical benefits: Used in medical, pharmaceutical and personal care preparations, mainly as a means of improving smoothness, providing lubrication and as a humectant. It is found in cough syrups, elixirs and expectorants, toothpaste and mouthwashes.

Should you be scared of it? No.

ADI (Acceptable Daily Intake): Not specified.

E425(i)

Konjac gum; Konjac glucomannan (Gelling agent, thickener, stabilizer)

These are extracted from the tubers of the *Amorphophallus konjac* plant, grown widely in India and the tropical Far East.

Use: They are used to produce gels and aspics, to bind sausage meats, to prevent food against freezer damage, to give cheeses a better mouthfeel and body, thickening and stabilizing a wide range of foods.

Natural version: Japanese konnyaku noodles (*shirataki*) and a Shicuan version of tofu (*moyu doufu*), made from konjac gluccomannan, have been traditional staple foods in the Far East for over a thousand years.

Likely products: Aspics; surimi (reformed fish and shellfish); ice cream and frozen desserts; meat products; cream cheese and processed cheese; sauces; gravies and batters; coatings; toppings and batters for baked goods and pasta.

Food scares: Konjac has been made into a popular Asian fruit jelly snack known as konjac candy in the USA and usually sold in bite-sized plastic cups. As konjac is highly viscous and does not dissolve in the mouth, it is easy for people, especially children, to choke on it.

Nutritional/medical benefits: It is very high in fibre but contains virtually no calories, so makes an excellent diet food.

Should you be scared of it? No, but note the above.

ADI (Acceptable Daily Intake): Not specified.

E426 🍎
Soybean hemicellulose (Emulsifier, thickener, stabilizer, anti-caking agent)

An extract of soya bean fibre that is available in many forms tailored to specific requirement and used for several purposes on a wide range of foods.

Use: Widely used in dairy-based drinks, food supplements and pre-packaged foods.

Natural version: Soya beans.

Likely products: Dairy-based drinks; emulsified sauces; noodles and rice products; fine baked goods; low-calorie breads and jellied confectionery.

Food scares: Many people are allergic to soya bean products, causing a wide range of effects from rashes to potentially fatal anaphylactic shock.

Nutritional/medical benefits: Soy products are high in essential omega-3 oils and in isoflavones, which are generally held to help fight cancers.

Should you be scared of it? No, but note the above.

ADI (Acceptable Daily Intake): Not specified.

E431
Polyoxyethylene (40) stearate (Emulsifier, anti-foaming agent)

A synthetic compound made from stearic acid that is not widely used.

Use: In wine making, to inhibit the production of foam during fermentation. Permitted only in wines produced outside the EU.
Likely products: Non-European wines.
Should you be scared of it? No.
ADI (Acceptable Daily Intake): 0–25 mg/kg bodyweight.

E432
Polyoxyethylene sorbitan monolaurate; Polysorbate 20 (Surfactant, emulsifier)

A synthetic chemical used as a surfactant (allowing substances to spread more easily and also for oil and water to mix together) as well as an emulsifier (allowing a substance to *stay* mixed).

Use: Forming oil-in-water emulsions for foods such as sauces and margarines, improving the volume and texture of cakes, helping coffee whiteners disperse and giving whipped cream the right texture.
Likely products: Cakes and cake mixes; coffee whiteners; whipped creams (dairy and vegetable fat); margarines; salad dressings and sauces.
Food scares: None at all but excessive levels of consumption. On an unverified list of suspected causes of birth defects, again at higher levels than additive use.
Should you be scared of it? No, but see above.
ADI (Acceptable Daily Intake): 0–25 mg/kg body weight.

E433
Polyoxyethylene sorbitan mono-oleate; Polysorbate 80 (Surfactant, emulsifier)
As E432.

Use: Much as E432, often in combination with other emulsifiers.
Likely products: Ice cream; frozen desserts; margarine; salad dressings and sauces.
Should you be scared of it? No.
ADI (Acceptable Daily Intake): 0–25 mg/kg body weight.

E434
Polyoxyethylene sorbitan monopalmitate; Polysorbate 40 (Emulsifier, surfactant)
As E432.

Use: Much as E432 and E433.
Likely products: Cakes and cake mixes; coffee whiteners; whipped creams (dairy and vegetable fat); desserts; confectionery; margarine; salad dressings and sauces.
Food scares: Used in very large amounts it can cause flatulence, diarrhoea and abdominal distension.
Should you be scared of it? No.
ADI (Acceptable Daily Intake): 0–25 mg/kg body weight.

E435
Polyoxyethylene sorbitan monostearate; Polysorbate 60 (Emulsifier)
As E432.

Use: As E432 and E433.
Likely products: Cakes and cake mixes; bread; coffee whiteners; whipped creams (dairy and vegetable fat); desserts; confectionery; margarine; salad dressings and sauces.

Should you be scared of it? No.
ADI (Acceptable Daily Intake): 0–25 mg/kg body weight.

E436
Polyoxyethylene sorbitan tristearate; Polysorbate 65 (Emulsifier, surfactant)
As E432.

Use: Much as E432 and E433.
Likely products: Ice cream; frozen desserts; confectionery; cakes and cake mixes; coffee whiteners and whipped creams (dairy and vegetable fats).
Should you be scared of it? No.
ADI (Acceptable Daily Intake): 0–25 mg/kg body weight.

E440 🍎
Pectins (Gelling agent, thickener, stabilizer)
Pectins are a family of compounds found in the cell walls of most land plants. Their ability to gel liquids has been well known to makers of jams and other preserves for centuries.

Use: As gelling and thickening agents in a wide range of mainly acid foods, often fruit-based, as well as in glazes and sauces for savoury products. Another use is to improve the mouthfeel of drinks, especially low-calorie ones.
Source: Most pectins come from fruits that have already been juiced, especially apple and citrus peel. The pulp of beetroots left over after they have had their sugar extracted is another major source.
Natural version: Fruits and vegetables.
Likely products: Jams and marmalades; confectionery; bakery fillings and toppings, such as Ross Blackcurrant Cheesecake; fruit yoghurts and jellies; ready meal glazes and sauces; yoghurt drinks and soft drinks.
Food scares: These can cause stomach problems in high quantities.
Nutritional/medical benefits: Used against constipation and diarrhoea.
Should you be scared of it? No, but note the above.
ADI (Acceptable Daily Intake): Not specified.

E442
Ammonium phosphatides; Emulsifier YN; Ammonium salts of phosphorylated glycerides (Emulsifier, stabilizer)

These are made from edible fats, usually hydrogenated rapeseed oil.

Use: As an emulsifier, mostly for the chocolate industry (it is the one used in Cadbury's Dairy Milk) where it is used to reduce the viscosity of the liquid chocolate, thus making it more suitable for handling, enrobing and moulding, etc.

Likely products: Chocolate; ice cream coatings; confectionery; fillings; drinking chocolate and chocolate spreads.

Should you be scared of them? No.

ADI (Acceptable Daily Intake): 0–20 mg/kg body weight

E444
Sucrose acetate isobutyrate (Emulsifier)

A synthetic compound made from sugar.

Use: Used primarily as an emulsifier to prevent small particles of essential oil flavourings from coalescing and separating out of cloudy soft drinks.

Likely products: Cloudy soft drinks.

Should you be scared of it? No.

ADI (Acceptable Daily Intake): 0–20 mg/kg body weight.

E445
Glycerol esters wood rosin; Ester gum (Emulsifier)

A pale yellow material extracted from pine wood chips.

Use: As E444.

Likely products: Cloudy soft drinks and chewing gum.

Should you be scared of it? No.

ADI (Acceptable Daily Intake): 0–25 mg/kg body weight.

E450 🍎
Diphosphates: Disodium diphosphate; Trisodium diphosphate; Tetrasodium diphosphate; Tetrapotassium diphosphate; Dicalcium diphosphate; Calcium dihydrogen diphosphate (Raising agents, stabilizers)

Diphosphates are derived from yellow phosphorus found in phosphate rock, which is then burned at high temperatures to create phosphorus pentoxide, which is then treated with sodium, potassium or calcium hydroxide and undergoes further chemical treatment.

Use: As raising agents in baked goods though they can leave an aftertaste (think brilliantly risen scones which leave your mouth feeling dry). They also have an emulsifying action, which is employed in the manufacture of processed cheese. In meats they retain moisture and this is used to add water to some processed meats and thus provide succulence, a practice for which food lobbyists have requested more regulation.

Likely products: Baked products and baking powders; meats; processed cheese and cheese sauces; milk-based drinks and beverage whiteners; powdered foods and icing sugars.

Should you be scared of them? No.

ADI (Acceptable Daily Intake): 0–70 mg/kg body weight.

E451 🍎
Triphosphates: Pentasodium triphosphate; Pentapotassium triphosphate

E452 🍎
Polyphosphates: Sodium polyphosphate; Potassium polyphosphate; Sodium calcium polyphosphate; Calcium polyphosphate (Emulsifiers, stabilizers, sequestrants, texturisers)

Triphosphates are derived from yellow phosphorus found in phosphate rock, which is then burned at high temperatures to create phosphorus pentoxide, which is then treated with sodium, potassium or calcium hydroxide and undergoes further chemical treatment.

Use: The emulsification role of these phosphates is important in the production of processed cheese and cheese based products such as sauces, where they prevent the fat and liquid separating out. In the fish industry they are used to prevent 'drip' which leads to the loss of moisture so the fish doesn't dry out during processing. In meat processing they combine with salt to retain water and help bind pieces of meat together, as in canned meatloaf.

Likely products: Processed meats such as ham and other deli meats; fish and seafood; processed cheese; sauces; beverage whiteners; ices; icing sugars; dried powdered foods and milk-based drinks.

Should you be scared of them? No.

ADI (Acceptable Daily Intake): 0–70 mg/kg body weight.

E459
Beta-cyclodextrin (Flavour carrier)

A type of carbohydrate, this is an expensive additive so is rarely used, but has the benefit of encapsulating flavour so the food can be heat-treated without the flavour disappearing.

Use: Used in dehydrated foods such as instant drinks or flavoured snacks as it traps the flavour and permits high heat treatment without damage to the delicate flavours.

Likely products: Sugarless confectionery, extruded snacks, and frozen meals; extending the shelf lives of foods with flavours, such as orange and lime, that oxidize readily.

Should you be scared of it? No.

ADI (Acceptable Daily Intake): None allocated.

E460 ❧
Cellulose: Microcrystalline cellulose; Powdered cellulose (Binding agent, gelling agent, emulsifier, stabilizer)

Both forms of cellulose used as food additives are made from the natural cellulose that gives plants and trees their structure.

Use: Powdered cellulose can bind 4–9 times its own weight of water, so it is used to protect against freeze-thaw damage in frozen food and to improve the flow properties of pancake batters. It also helps retain moisture, reduce fat uptake and improve crumb structure in cakes, muffins and doughnuts. Microcrystalline cellulose is used with guar gum to give body and creaminess to low-fat foods such as dressings, mayonnaise and milk drinks.

Likely products: Puffed snack foods; baked goods; instant foods; diet foods; milk drinks; processed cheeses; pancake batters; whipping cream; mayonnaise; frozen desserts and reformed meats.

Food scares: Large concentrations can cause intestinal problems, such as bloating, constipation and diarrhoea.

Should you be scared of it? No, not at additive levels.

ADI (Acceptable Daily Intake): Not specified.

E461
Methyl cellulose (Thickener, binding agent, gelling agent, stabilizer, emulsifier)

A synthetic compound made from cellulose.

Use: It is primarily used for its gelling and binding properties, especially for improving shape retention in reformed meat and potato products. It also helps deep-fried products from absorbing too much oil.

Likely products: Soya burgers, sausages and other formed products; onion rings, potato croquettes, waffles and other formed potato products; gluten-free baked goods; batters and coatings; doughnuts and low-fat dairy products.

Food scares: As E460.

Nutritional/medical benefits: It is used to treat constipation and used as a substitute for artificial tears.

Should you be scared of it? No, but note the above.

ADI (Acceptable Daily Intake): Not specified.

E462
Ethyl cellulose
(Thickener, binder, gelling agent, emulsifier)

This is manufactured by treating wood pulp or cotton with chemicals.

Use: Used as a bulking and raising agent, and to help fix flavours.
Likely products: Mostly food supplements and flavourings.
Food scares: As E460.
Should you be scared of it? No, but note the above.
ADI (Acceptable Daily Intake): Not specified.

E463
Hydroxypropyl cellulose
(Thickener, stabilizer, emulsifier)

A synthetic chemical made from cellulose.

Use: It is used as a stabilizer in aerated products and as a thickener in alcoholic drinks.
Likely products: Aerated toppings, especially those using creams, and some alcoholic drinks.
Food scares: As E460.
Nutritional/medical benefits: Used for artificial tears. Oddly enough, I have a small bottle of it right here on my desk, that I'm using (unsuccessfully) to cure my gammy eye. Also used to treat medical conditions characterized by insufficient tear production, recurrent corneal erosions and decreased corneal sensitivity. Also used as a laxative.
Should you be scared of it? No, but note the above.
ADI (Acceptable Daily Intake): Not specified.

E464
Hydroxypropyl methyl cellulose
(Thickener, emulsifier, stabilizer)
A synthetic chemical made from cellulose.

Use: As E461. It is also used as a vegetarian alternative to animal gelatin.
Likely products: Soya burgers, sausages and other formed products, onion rings, potato croquettes, waffles and other formed potato products, gluten-fee baked goods, batters and coatings, doughnuts, low-fat dairy products.
Food scares: As E 460.
Nutritional/medical benefits: As E463.
Should you be scared of it? No, but note the above.
ADI (Acceptable Daily Intake): Not specified.

E465
Methylethyl cellulose
(Thickener, stabilizer, emulsifier, foaming agent)
A synthetic chemical made from cellulose.

Use: As E461.
Likely products: Soya burgers, sausages and other formed products; onion rings, potato croquettes, waffles and other formed potato products; gluten-fee baked goods; batters and coatings; doughnuts, low-fat dairy products.
Food scares: As E460.
Should you be scared of it? No, note the above.
ADI (Acceptable Daily Intake): Not specified.

E466
Carboxymethyl cellulose
(Thickener, stabilizer, emulsifier)

A synthetic chemical made from cellulose.

Use: Mostly as a thickener in drinks, sauces and toppings, and in the powdered forms of these products, as a stabilizer in fruit pulps, drinks and concentrates, and as a water binder in baking.

Likely products: Soft drinks (such as Sunny Delight); dairy drinks, powders and concentrates for drinks; sauces and dressings; ice creams and water ices; baked produce; dairy products and soy products.

Food scares: As E460.

Nutritional/medical benefits: Helps lower blood cholesterol levels and is used as laxative. Used in artificial tears.

Should you be scared of it? No, but note the above.

ADI (Acceptable Daily Intake): None allocated.

E468
Crosslinked sodium carboxymethyl cellulose
(Thickener, disintegration agent)

A synthetic chemical made from cellulose.

Use: A disintegration agent to hasten the break-up, dispersion or dissolution in water of tablets, capsules or granules.

Likely products: Artificial sweetener tablets, solid dietary supplements, such as vitamin, mineral and fibre tablets.

Food scares: As E460.

Nutritional/medical benefits: Slightly lowers blood cholesterol levels.

Should you be scared of it? No, but note the above.

ADI (Acceptable Daily Intake): Not specified.

E469
Enzymatically hydrolysed carboxy methyl cellulose (Glazing agent, carrier, stabilizer, thickener)

A synthetic chemical made from cellulose.

Use: There is currently no commercial production of this material.
ADI (Acceptable Daily Intake): Not specified.

E470a ● ♀
Sodium, potassium and calcium salts of fatty acids (Anti-caking agents, defoaming agents)

A synthetic chemical made from fatty acids, see E570.

Use: To decrease foaming during the processing of beetroots to obtain sugar, to lessen the stickiness of chewing gum and to promote yeast activity.
Likely products: Beet sugar, chewing gum, cake mixes and oven chips.
Food scares: Very high doses can interfere with intestinal functions.
Should you be scared of it? No, but note the above.
ADI (Acceptable Daily Intake): None allocated.

E470b ●
Magnesium salts of fatty acids (Anti-caking agent, emulsifier)

A synthetic chemical made from fatty acids, see E570.

Use: Mostly in the making of tablets to help powders flow.
Likely products: Tablets.
Should you be scared of it? No.
ADI (Acceptable Daily Intake): None allocated.

E471 🍎
Mono- and diglycerides of fatty acids (Emulsifiers)

These are natural compounds found in the fats of the food we eat and produced by the body's digestion of fats. The types used as additives are, however, made chemically from triglyceride fats or glycerol.

Use: These are possibly the most important of the food emulsifiers as they account for about 50% of the total food emulsifier market in Europe and are the type most used in bread as they keep the gluten pliable to get a good final texture.

Likely products: Bread, cakes and other baked goods; cereals; puddings; fresh pasta; instant mashed potatoes; frozen desserts; whipped toppings; ice creams; confectionery; chewing gum; fats such as margarines and shortenings.

Should you be scared of it? No.

ADI (Acceptable Daily Intake): 0–30 mg/kg body weight.

E472a 🍎
Acetic acid esters of mono- and diglycerides of fatty acids (acetems) (Emulsifiers, aerating agents, stabilizers, anti-foaming agents)

These are compounds created by reacting mono- and diglycerides of fatty acids (E471), from plant or animal origin, with acetic acid (E260) from synthetic or fermented sources. They come in a wide range of forms, solid, liquid and pastes, and with a wide range of melting points depending on the fatty acids used.

Use: As emulsifiers and aerating agents for cakes, sponges and whipped toppings; as emulsifiers and stabilizers for foams of protein, fat and sugar; coating and protecting foods such as sausages, fruit and cheese; to prevent foaming in jams; adjusting the melting points and plasticity of fats.

Likely products: Cakes and sponges; whipped toppings and mousses such as Cadbury's and Müllerlight mousse desserts and Marks & Spencer Strawberry Trifle; chewing gum; sausages and other meat products; fruit; cheese; jams and marmalades and fats.

Should you be scared of it? No.

ADI (Acceptable Daily Intake): None allocated.

E472b ♥ ⚲

Lactic acid esters of mono- and diglycerides of fatty acids (lactems) (Emulsifiers, aerating agents)

These are compounds created by reacting mono- and diglycerides of fatty acids (E471), from plant or animal origin, with lactic acid (E270) from synthetic or fermented sources. They come in a wide range of forms, solid, liquid and pastes, and with a wide range of melting points depending on the fatty acids used.

Use: As emulsifiers and aerating agents for cakes, sponges and whipped toppings; adjusting the melting points and plasticity of fats.
Likely products: Cake sponges; whipped toppings; mousses; margarines.
Food scares: There was some concern that these might be carcinogenic, but it appears to be baseless.
Should you be scared of it? No.
ADI (Acceptable Daily Intake): None allocated.

E472c ♥

Citric acid esters of mono- and diglycerides of fatty acids (citrems) (Emulsifiers, stabilizers)

These are compounds created by reacting mono- and diglycerides of fatty acids (E471), from plant or animal origin, with citric acid (E330) from fermented sources. They come in a wide range of forms, solid, liquid and pastes, and with a wide range of melting points depending on the fatty acids used.

Use: As emulsifiers to prevent separation of fats during cutting or chopping and to stabilize emulsions in cooked products such as liver sausage; to reduce spattering of margarines used for frying. Some are used to protect yeast cells when they are being dried.
Likely products: Sausages, frying margarines, cocoa and chocolate products, dried yeast.
Food scares: There was some concern that these might be carcinogenic, but it appears to be baseless.
Should you be scared of it? No.
ADI (Acceptable Daily Intake): None allocated.

E472d ❦
Tartaric acid esters of mono- and diglycerides of fatty acids (tatems) (Emulsifier, stabilizer)

These are compounds created by reacting mono- and diglycerides of fatty acids (E471), from plant or animal origin, with tartaric acid, a by-product of wine-making. They come in a wide range of forms, solid, liquid and pastes, and with a wide range of melting points depending on the fatty acids used.

Use: As tartaric acid is relatively expensive, this is the most expensive of the E472 group, so is little used.
Should you be scared of it? No.
ADI (Acceptable Daily Intake): None allocated.

E472e
Mono- and diacetyl tartaric acid esters of mono- and diglycerides of fatty acids (datems) (Emulsifier, stabilizer)

These are compounds created by reacting mono- and diglycerides of fatty acids (E471), from plant or animal origin, with tartaric acid, a by-product of wine-making, and adding other chemicals. They come in a wide range of forms, solid, liquid and pastes, and with a wide range of melting points depending on the fatty acids used.

Use: As emulsifiers in a wide range of food products, particularly with proteins, as in wheat-based baked goods (in which they improve the dough's performance in several ways), and in egg-based emulsions, where they make them less prone to coagulation.
Likely products: Baked goods, mayonnaise and other emulsions containing egg.
Should you be scared of it? Not unless you make a scary cake.
ADI (Acceptable Daily Intake): None allocated.

E472f
Mixed acetic and tartaric acid esters of mono- and diglycerides of fatty acids (matems)
(Emulsifier, stabilizer)

These are compounds created by reacting mono- and diglycerides of fatty acids (E471), from plant or animal origin, with a mixture of acetic and tartaric acids in various proportions, and adding other chemicals. They come in a wide range of forms, solid, liquid and pastes, and with a wide range of melting points depending on the fatty acids used and the proportions of each acid.

Use: As E472e, this improves doughs.
Should you be scared of it? No.
ADI (Acceptable Daily Intake): None allocated.

E473 🍎 ⚊
Sucrose esters of fatty acids
(Emulsifier, stabilizer)

Made from fatty acids that may be plant or animal in origin, these compounds are great emulsifiers, preventing the separation of fat and oils. They can withstand very high temperatures, so are particularly useful in powders used for hot drinks, such as coffee whiteners.

Use: As an emulsifier or to prevent foams from collapsing.
Likely products: Powdered drinks and coffee whiteners, high-quality bakery products and ice cream.
Should you be scared of it? No.
ADI (Acceptable Daily Intake): 0–30 mg/kg body weight.

E474 🍎
Sucroglycerides (Emulsifier, stabilizer)

Made from natural oils such as coconut, rapeseed, or palm oil and sugars (not all the oils may be plant in origin, so vegetarians may want to avoid), this food additive is an emulsifier (preventing the separation of fat and oils), and also helps improve texture and control crystallization – a very important issue in products such as ice cream.

Use: As an emulsifier to maintain structure in foods.
Likely products: Ice cream, drinks and baked goods.
Should you be scared of it? No.
ADI (Acceptable Daily Intake): 0–30 mg/kg body weight.

E475
Polyglycerol esters of fatty acids (Emulsifier, stabilizer)

Made from glycerol (E422) and fatty acids which may be plant or animal in origin, this additive is widely used as an emulsifier (preventing the separation of fat and oils) in low fat spreads as it helps prevent the fat from 'weeping' liquid and means less overall fat can be used.

Use: Used as an emulsifier to maintain texture and structure in foods and stop fats from separating.
Likely products: Cakes, frozen cheesecake, chewing gum, gateaux.
Should you be scared of it? No.
ADI (Acceptable Daily Intake): 0–25 mg/kg body weight.

E476
Polyglycerol polyricinoleate (PGPR) (Emulsifier, stabilizer)

E476 is made from castor oil, which comes from the castor oil tree and glycerol (E422). It is used to control the texture of chocolate and cocoa based products, particularly during processing when they are liquid so that they can flow more easily when melted. There are some concerns that it may be used to replace cocoa butter in chocolate, as it is a cheaper alternative to a more costly ingredient.

Use: Used mainly to help the flow of liquid chocolate in its manufacture and prevent unwanted bubbling, and also used in the production of low fat spreads.
Likely products: Chocolate and cocoa products, low-fat spreads.
Should you be scared of it? No.
ADI (Acceptable Daily Intake): None set.

E477
Propane 1,2 diol esters of fatty acids (Emulsifier, stabilizer)

Made from an oil that provides the fatty acids, along with propylene glycol (E1520), E477 are emulsifiers (they prevent the separation of fat and oils). They help cake and dessert mixes to be whipped, and they are often used in conjunction with other emulsifiers to enhance the effect.

Use: As emulsifiers.
Likely products: Used mainly in cakes and powdered desserts.
Should you be scared of it? No.
ADI (Acceptable Daily Intake): None set.

E479b
Thermally oxidised soya-bean oil interacted with mono and diglycerides of fatty acids (Emulsifier)

Despite winning the prize for the longest name, this additive is one of the least used. Made from soya oil plus a reaction with E471 or a similar compound, it prevents emulsions which are fried on a hot plate or griddle from separating out and burning and also prevents them from sticking.

Use: As an emulsifier.
Should you be scared of it? No.
ADI (Acceptable Daily Intake): None set.

E481
Sodium stearoyl-2 lactylate

E482
Calcium stearoyl-2 lactylate
(Emulsifiers, stabilizers)

These emulsifiers are made from a combination of lactic and stearic acids, both of which are naturally present in many foods, although stearic acid can be derived from animal products.

Use: Used as emulsifiers in coffee whiteners, which are spray-dried during processing, and also used in bread dough to help with texture of the crumb.

Likely products: Coffee whiteners, bread and low-fat spreads.
Should you be scared of it? No.
ADI (Acceptable Daily Intake): None set.

E483
Stearyl tartrate (Emulsifier, stabilizer)

Made from tartaric acid (E334) and stearyl alcohol (which is itself based on stearic acid), this is used in bread and bakery products as an emulsifier.

Use: As an emulsifier in flour.
Likely products: Bread and baked goods.
Should you be scared of it? No.
ADI (Acceptable Daily Intake): 0–500 mg/kg of flour.

E491
Sorbitan monostearate

E492
Sorbitan tristearate

E493
Sorbitan monolaurate

E494
Sorbitan monooleate

E495
Sorbitan monopalmitate
(Emulsifiers, stabilizers, glazing agents, anti-foaming agents)

Made from stearic, oleic, or palmitic fatty acids plus a compound derived from sorbitol (E420), this group of food additives are useful emulsifiers as they help distribute water-based compounds throughout an oily mixture. Ice cream is a good example of this.

Use: As emulsifiers.

Likely products: Ice creams; fat spread; cake mixes and chocolate production.

Should you be scared of them? No.

ADI (Acceptable Daily Intake): 0–25 mg/kg body weight.

E500 🍎

Sodium carbonates: Sodium carbonate; Sodium hydrogen carbonate (sodium bicarbonate or bicarbonate of soda or baking soda); Sodium sesquicarbonate (Leavening agents, buffers)

Sodium bicarbonate is made industrially from brine and limestone, while sodium carbonate is made from the bicarbonate and sodium sesquicarbonate is mined in the USA, where it is called 'trona'.

Use: Sodium bicarbonate is the main constituent of most baking powders where, together with tartaric or another acid, it will generate carbon dioxide when heated. The other two carbonates also work as raising agents in much the same way.

Likely products: Baked goods, including cakes such as Ross Blackcurrant Cheesecake and Bird's Eye Chicken Pies; scones, waffles, pastries and biscuits.

Nutritional/medical benefits: E500 sodium hydrogen carbonate is sometimes used as an antacid for heartburn or indigestion.

Should you be scared of them? Not unless you make a scary cake.

ADI (Acceptable Daily Intake): Unlimited.

E501

Potassium carbonates; Potassium hydrogen carbonate (Raising agents, acidity regulators, flavour enhancers)

Made by bubbling carbon dioxide into a solution of potassium hydroxide.

Use: Used mostly in baking powder or in products where low sodium (salt) is desirable. As they are more expensive than sodium-based baking powders, however, they are less used. Potassium carbonate also features in beer making, in the processing of the hops, and in the alkalization of cocoa powder.

Likely products: Baking and baking powder, biscuits and energy bars, low-sodium crackers, cocoa powder and chocolate drinks, convenience foods such as Chicken and Mushroom Pot Noodle, beer.

Should you be scared of them? No.

ADI (Acceptable Daily Intake): Unlimited.

E503

Ammonium carbonates; Ammonium hydrogen carbonate (bicarbonate)(Raising agents, acidity regulators)

Made by passing carbon dioxide through ammonia, with subsequent processing, like the other carbonates, ammonium carbonate is used mostly for its ability to leaven or raise bakery by producing carbon dioxide.

Use: As a raising agent in baked goods and as an alkali in the processing of cocoa powder.
Likely products: Baking powders and baked goods such as Ross Blackcurrant Cheesecake, biscuits, crackers and sugar confectionery, cocoa and chocolate products, such as KP Choc Dips.
Should you be scared of them? No.
ADI (Acceptable Daily Intake): Not specfied.

E504

Magnesium carbonates: Magnesium carbonate; Magnesium hydrogen carbonate (bicarbonate) (Raising agent, mineral source, free-flow agent)

Magnesium carbonate is made from dolomite, a naturally occurring mineral, while magnesium bicarbonate is made synthetically.

Use: You are most likely to find magnesium carbonate in table salt where is it used as a free flow agent as it resists water, though if you are a climber or weightlifter you may know it as the chalk used as a drying agent for your hands. It is also a raising agent and an inexpensive source of magnesium in fortified foods.
Likely products: Cheese, ice cream and table salt, as well as supplements and foods fortified with magnesium.
Nutritional/medical benefits: It is widely used as an antacid. Magnesium is an essential element in the body being found in bone and all cells.
Should you be scared of them? No.
ADI (Acceptable Daily Intake): Not specfied.

E507 🍎 ⚤

Hydrochoric acid (Acid)

Hydrochloric acid is found in the stomach and is essential for the digestion of protein, so although we may associate this additive with the chemistry lab it is found naturally in living organisms. Commercially it is made from salt.

Use: Because of its acid nature, it affects protein so it used in the production of vegetarian sources of protein such as soya mince. It is also used to make syrups from sugar.

Likely products: Syrups and hydrolysed vegetable protein foods, such as soya mince.

Should you be scared of it? No.

ADI (Acceptable Daily Intake): Not limited.

E508 🍎 ⚤

Potassium chloride (Flavour enhancer)

The potassium salt of hydrochloric acid, it is obtained by purification of a natural mineral source.

Use: As it is similar in taste to common salt (sodium chloride), it is used where a low-sodium (salt) diet or foods are required.

Likely products: Table-top salt replacers, convenience foods such as Chicken and Mushroom Pot Noodle and Prawn Cocktail Pringles, some dietetically controlled products.

Nutritional/medical benefits: May be helpful for those wanting to decrease their intake of salt (sodium chloride), such as hypertensives and kidney patients.

Should you be scared of it? No.

ADI (Acceptable Daily Intake): Unlimited.

E509 🍎 👤

Calcium chloride (Source of calcium ions, firming agent, coagulant)

The calcium salt of hydrochloric acid, it is extracted from natural brines or obtained as a by-product of the production of sodium carbonate.

Use: Calcium chloride is used for its ability to let go of its calcium and this improves the texture of products. It is used in the canning and bottling industry to keep vegetables firm, and in the brewing industry to modify the hardness of water. It is also used in cheese making.

Likely products: Canned and bottled fruit and vegetables, beer, olives, pickles and cheese.

Should you be scared of it? No.

ADI (Acceptable Daily Intake): Unlimited.

E511 🍎

Magnesium chloride (Firming agent, colour retention agent)

Obtained naturally from mineral ores and underground brines, this is also made from the mineral dolomite in reaction with hydrochloric acid.

Use: Fortifying foods with magnesium, and water preparation in brewing.

Likely products: Dietary supplements.

Should you be scared of it? No.

ADI (Acceptable Daily Intake): Unlimited.

E512

Stannous chloride; Tin dichloride (Colour retention agent, antioxidant)

This little-used additive is actually tin chloride made by reacting tin with chlorine or hydrochloric acid.

Use: Limited to the bottling and canning of white asparagus where it retains the pale colour of the vegetable.

Likely products: Canned or bottled white asparagus only.

Should you be scared of it? It has been associated with irritation in the stomach, and since its use is limited to one product, you are highly unlikely to suffer any negative effects unless you eat an *awful* lot of canned white asparagus.

ADI (Acceptable Daily Intake): A provisional tolerable weekly intake was set at 14 mg/kg body weight.

E513
Sulphuric acid (Acid)

A strong mineral acid made industrially from sulphur dioxide.

Use: To increase the acidity of foods during processing and in making invert sugar and syrups.

Likely products: Invert sugar and syrups.

Should you be scared of it? No. It sounds scary, but its presence in food is so fractional that it poses no risk.

ADI (Acceptable Daily Intake): Not specified.

E514
Sodium sulphate; Sodium hydrogen sulphate (sodium bisulphate) (Colour regulator, acid, antioxidant, preservative)

The sodium salts of sulphuric acid. Sodium sulphate occurs naturally and is mined as Glauber's salt. The bisulphate is the by-product of several processes involving sulphuric acid.

Use: Sodium sulphate is most commonly used to help fix dyes in the textile industry and as a standardizer in washing powder. It is also permitted in food products to ensure food colours act uniformly regardless of whether or not the colours are synthetic or natural. Sodium bisulphate is generally used as the acid in raising agents.

Likely products: Chewing gum; baked goods; beverages; dressings; sauces and fillings. It is also widely used in meat and poultry processing and most recently in browning prevention of fresh cut produce.

Should you be scared of it? No.

ADI (Acceptable Daily Intake): Not specified.

E515
Potassium sulphate; Potassium hydrogen sulphate (bisulphate) (Salt replacer, acid)

The potassium salts of sulphuric acid, both are made from sulphuric acid.

Use: The sulphate bisulphate is used as an acid in raising agents when sodium cannot be used and commonly used in the conversion of tartrates to bitartrates in wine.

Likely products: Baked goods, low-sodium salt replacers and some wines.

Should you be scared of it? No.

ADI (Acceptable Daily Intake): Not specified.

E516
Calcium sulphate; Plaster of Paris (Source of calcium, stabilizer, yeast conditioner, dough conditioner)

A naturally occurring mineral, it is also a by-product of several manufacturing processes.

Use: To prepare water for use in brewing beers, to keep canned vegetables and fruit firm, and to help stabilise bubbles in baked goods. As a stabilizer, it is also used in making tofu.

Likely products: Beer; bread; wafer biscuits; canned fruit and vegetables, tofu.

Nutritional/medical benefits: In its laboratory form it may help you if you have a fracture and need it to be plastered.

Should you be scared of it? No.

ADI (Acceptable Daily Intake): Unlimited.

E517
Ammonium sulphate
(Carrier, dispersant, acidity regulator)

Made by bubbling ammonia into sulphuric acid.

Use: Ammonium sulphate is permitted to be used a carrier for other additives, that is to say it disperses or dissolves the other additives without influencing its effect. It is also used to modify acidity in food products.
Likely products: None currently known.
Should you be scared of it? No.
ADI (Acceptable Daily Intake): None specified.

E520
Aluminium sulphate

E521
Aluminium sodium sulphate

E522
Aluminium potassium sulphate

E523
Aluminium ammonium sulphate
(Firming agents, buffers, raising agents, colour fixers)

You've probably heard of alum – this is aluminium sulphate. Made from the reaction of sulphuric acids with aluminium oxides or as a by-product of alcohol manufacture. It is not commonly used in foods and its use is strictly regulated, as aluminium is not an ideal component of any diet.

Use: It can only be used in two ways, firstly for dried egg white to help it retain its whipping qualities after reconstitution and secondly in crystallized fruit and vegetables.
Likely products: Dried egg white and crystallized fruit and vegetables.
Food scares: None related to aluminium sulphate.
Should you be scared of them? No.
ADI (Acceptable Daily Intake): 0–7 mg/kg body weight.

E524
Sodium hydroxide

E525
Potassium hydroxide
(Acidity regulators)

Sodium hydroxide is made industrially from salt; potassium hydroxide from naturally occurring potassium chloride.

Use: Sodium hydroxide, or caustic soda as it is better known, is a strong alkali, but food-grade solutions of it are used to dissolve peel in the potato and vegetable processing industry and there are a host of other historic and contemporary uses. These include brushing E524 on pretzels prior to baking to provide the crisp crust, and soaking dried maize in 'lye' water before processing to make 'grits'. Its role as an alkali is employed to stop the reaction in the process of producing invert sugar. It is also used in the cocoa industry as an alkali. Olives are sometimes left to soak in it to soften them before bottling. Potassium hydroxide has the same functions and is just used where there is a need to limit the amount of sodium in the product.

Likely products: Cocoa powder and chocolate beverages; jam; invert sugar; milk drinks; baked good including pretzels; olives; processed vegetables, especially potatoes, and grits.

Should you be scared of them? No.

ADI (Acceptable Daily Intake): Unlimited.

E526
Calcium hydroxide (Firming agent, buffer, neutralizing agent)

Made industrially from the addition of water to calcium oxide.

Use: Otherwise known as slaked lime, calcium hydroxide is used in the purification of sugar, and also as a firming agent in jam making. Fruit contains pectin which helps jam to set, and calcium hydroxide combines with the pectin to preserve the fruit texture. It may also be found in dietary supplements as a source of calcium.

Likely products: Sugar, jams and preserves; dietary supplements.

Should you be scared of it? No.

ADI (Acceptable Daily Intake): Unlimited.

E527
Ammonium hydroxide (Acidity regulator)

Made by passing ammonia gas through water.

Use: This is a strong alkali, which can be used to alter the acidity of foods during processing.

Source: It is made by passing ammonia gas into water.

Likely products: Very few, but might be found in some cocoa products.

Should you be scared of it? No.

ADI (Acceptable Daily Intake): Unlimited.

E528
Magnesium hydroxide (Acidity regulator, mineral source, colour moderator)

Made from the natural ore dolomite or extracted from seawater. You may be more familiar with Milk of Magnesia than with E528, but they are one and the same thing.

Use: In foods E528 is used for its alkalinity in cheese processing, and in vegetable canning to preserve colour.

Likely products: Some cheeses and canned vegetables, food supplements.
Should you be scared of it? No.
ADI (Acceptable Daily Intake): Unlimited.

E529
Calcium oxide (Alkali, dough conditioner)

Made by heating limestone.

Use: For its calcium content in dietary supplements or fortified foods, but may also be used in bread making where it reacts with yeast as a dough conditioner, improving the bread.
Likely products: Fortified foods, bread and other baked goods, such as tortillas.
Nutritional/medical benefits: Only if used in fortified foods or supplements where the calcium may provide benefits.
Should you be scared of it? No.
ADI (Acceptable Daily Intake): Unlimited.

E530
Magnesium oxide (Anti-caking agent)

Made industrially by heating the natural ore dolomite, which contains magnesium carbonate.

Use: As an anti-caking agent, that is it prevents dry mixtures, like coco powder, from clumping together.
Likely products: Cocoa powder and chocolate beverages.
Should you be scared of it? No.
ADI (Acceptable Daily Intake): Unlimited.

E535
Sodium ferrocyanide

E536
Potassium ferrocyanide

E538
Calcium ferrocyanide
(Anti-caking agents)

With cyanide in their names it is understandable to approach this group of synthetic additives cautiously. However, they are only permitted at really very low levels in table salt.

Use: As an anti-caking agent in table salt, preventing the salt from clumping together.
Likely products: Some table salts.
Should you be scared of them? No.
ADI (Acceptable Daily Intake): 0–0.025 mg/kg body weight.

E541
Sodium aluminium phosphate (Raising agent, emulsifier)

A synthetic compound.

Use: This is another raising agent used when there is a delay between making and baking, as it doesn't release the carbon dioxide until it hits the oven, unlike bicarbonate of soda (E500).
Likely products: Scones, cakes and sponges.
Should you be scared of it? No.
ADI (Acceptable Daily Intake): 0–0.6 mg/kg body weight

E551 🍎
Silicon dioxide

E552
Calcium silicate

E553a
Magnesium silicate

E553b
Magnesium trisilicate; Talc
(Anti-caking agents, free-flow agents, thickeners, filtering aids, coating agents, texturizers)

All of these silica-based additives are fine powders. Silicon dioxide is found in nature as sand, but the food-grade version is synthetic and extremely fine. Magnesium trisilicate is better known as talc and is as naturally occurring form of magnesium silicate.

Use: As free-flow and anti-caking agents in powdered foods and drinks. As an anti-caking agent the silicates can be used up to 10g per kg of dried powdered foods, more (30g) in products designed to grease tins and up to 50g per kg in food flavours. E553b (talc) is a dusting agent that is also used to help with the release of baked goods from tins. The fineness of the powders allows them to be used to coat foods, such as ready-sliced cheeses, in order to prevent them sticking together. Talc is also used in some chewing gum bases.

Likely products: Powdered drinks and foods, sliced and grated cheeses, chewing gum.

Should you be scared of them? No.

ADI (Acceptable Daily Intake): Not specified.

E554
Sodium aluminium silicate

E555
Potassium aluminium silicate

E556
Calcium aluminium silicate
(Anti-caking agents)

Synthetic fine powders.

Use: Like the other silicates, these additives are also used as anti-caking and free-flow agents in powdered drinks and desserts. The most commonly used is the sodium-based additive.

Likely products: Dried foods and powdered drinks.

Should you be scared of them? No.

ADI (Acceptable Daily Intake): Not specified.

E558
Bentonite (Anti-caking agents, filtering agents, colour carriers)

E559
Kaolin (aluminium silicate)

Both these additives are made from naturally occurring clays used for their capacity to filter liquids.

Use: As well as filtering wines and fruit juices, Bentonite is used as a carrier for food colours and Kaolin is also used as an anti-caking agent in a powdered form.

Likely products: Kaolin may be found in instant coffee and milk powders.

Should you be scared of them? No.

ADI (Acceptable Daily Intake): None allocated.

E570 🍎 ↟
Fatty acids (Anti-foaming agents, anti-caking agents, texturizers)

There are many different fatty acids naturally present in the fats we eat as all fats and oils are made up of a wide range of different fatty acids attached to glycerol (E422). The fatty acids permitted as E570 may be stearic, palmitic and oleic acids which are naturally found in fats from plant and animal foods. These fatty acids are usually prepared from plant oils but making them from animal fats such as tallow can't be ruled out, so vegetarians may want to avoid them. In cocoa butter nearly half the fatty acids are stearic acid.

Use: Fatty acids are used to prevent foaming in jam – if you make your own you'll know that dropping a knob of butter in the pan at the end of preparation will reduce foaming. They are also used in chewing gum for their effect on texture.

Likely products: Chewing gum.

Should you be scared of it? No, these are natural and found in many fats and oils.

ADI: (Acceptable Daily Intake): Present uses are safe and not of toxicological concern.

E574 🍎 ↟
Gluconic acid (Acid)

Made from glucose, which is made from starch, gluconic acid is found in fruits, honey, and wine. As its name suggests, it is related to glucose and is used in foods and drinks where a mild acid is required.

Use: As a source of acid where stronger citric and malic acids would spoil the flavour or make the food too acidic.

Likely products: Fruit drinks and juices, and other fruit-based products.

Should you be scared of it? No.

ADI (Acceptable Daily Intake): Not specified.

E575
Glucono-delta-lactone (GdL)(Acid, coagulant, raising agent)

This odd-sounding but useful additive is naturally present in a number of foods, including wine, honey and fruit. It is used as a curing, pickling, coagulant and raising agent.

Use: GdL is used to curdle milk and soya for the production of cheese and tofu. It is also used as a raising agent with sodium bicarbonate (E500), and can bind iron and copper in products where they are not required.

Likely products: Soft cheeses including feta, mozzarella and cottage cheese; sausages; bread mixes and ready-to-cook doughs. Also found in canned seafood.

Should you be scared of it? No – it is metabolized in the body as glucose.

ADI (Acceptable Daily Intake): Not specified.

E576
Sodium gluconate

E577
Potassium gluconate

E578
Calcium gluconate

E579
Ferrous gluconate
(Mineral supplements, flavour modifiers, gelling agents, firming agents, sequestrants, colour modifiers)

Made synthetically from gluconic acid (made from glucose) plus the appropriate metal in solution, this group of additives are often used to fortify products because they readily give up the metal part of the molecule, so calcium for example is released, and they don't have an unpleasant taste as they are based on a sugar (glucose) molecule.

Use: They may be used for fortification but each has other roles too. E576 is used to mask other flavours as in low-sugar products, especially those using saccharin. E577 readily gives up potassium so is used in sports or diet drinks where it also adjusts taste. E578 is used to set dessert mixes. The ferrous (iron) gluconate E579 is limited in its use to cause green olives to go black.

Source: Made synthetically from gluconic acid (made from glucose) plus the appropriate metal in solution.

Likely products: E576 – in low-sugar chewing gum.

E577 – in milky drinks, sports drinks, baked goods, and 'health' bars.

E578 – in drinks, dairy products and desserts.

E579 – in darkened olives.

Should you be scared of them? No.

ADI (Acceptable Daily Intake): For E576, E577 and 578 – not specified. For E579 a provisional maxiumum tolerable daily intake of 0–0.8 mg/kg body weight.

E585
Ferrous lactate (Colour modifier)

Made synthetically from ferrous sulphate and sodium lactate, this is another olive-darkening additive. E585 or ferrous (iron) lactate can be metabolized by the body.

Use: To darken green olives.

Likely products: Dark-coloured olives.

Should you be scared of it? No.

ADI (Acceptable Daily Intake): Provisional maximum tolerable daily intake of 0–0.8 mg/kg body weight.

E586
4-Hexylresorcinol (Antioxidant)

A synthetic compound with anaesthetic, antiseptic and antioxidant properties.

Use: Prevents black melanoma spots from appearing on the shells of crustaceans.
Likely products: Fresh and frozen crustacea.
Nutritional/medical benefits: Used topically on small skin infections and in throat lozenges.
Should you be scared of it? No.
ADI (Acceptable Daily Intake): None allocated.

E620 🍎 ♀
Glutamic acid

E621
Monosodium glutamate

E622
Monopotassium glutamate

E623
Calcium diglutamate

E624
Monoammonium glutamate

E625
Magnesium diglutamate (Flavour enhancers)

Naturally present in many foods, such as meat, fish, poultry and cheese, glutamic acid is a component of proteins as it is an amino acid. Glutamates, compounds (naturally) made from glutamic acid, have many functions in the body including in the nervous system and brain.

Glutamate is responsible for the fifth flavour known as 'umami' and was identified by a Japanese professor in 1907 who then went on to develop a synthetic version – monosodium glutamate (MSG).

Only E621, monosodium glutamate is used to any extent as a food additive. It is made from the fermentation of starch or molasses.

MSG is an additive with a colourful history. It was said to cause 'Chinese Restaurant Syndrome' as early as 1968, the symptoms being similar to a mild allergic reaction, such as an increase in asthmatic symptoms and itchiness. There have been many well-conducted studies that have looked at the relationship between MSG and these symptoms. These have included double-blind placebo-controlled trials (the gold standard of clinical trials, where neither the researcher nor the participant knows whether they are receiving the active ingredient or a dummy), as well as trials using individuals who are had previously reacted to MSG, who don't consistently have a reaction in trials. So perhaps surprisingly, given its notoriety, despite decades of research there has yet to be a clearly demonstrated consistent relationship between eating MSG and developing allergic reactions. So while some individuals genuinely say they get symptoms when eating MSG, these symptoms cannot consistently be replicated in clinical trials. Trials have also been carried out on people said to be suffering from headaches, dizziness and other (neurological) problems after eating MSG. It was found that these problems were due to the increased amount of sodium that eating MSG provided and not drinking sufficient liquid, producing what was called the 'hangover effect'. So, again, no consistently clear relationship could be established with the intake of MSG and these symptoms.

You may reasonably ask therefore why manufacturers are keen to proclaim the absence of MSG from food products. The answer lies in the perceived consumer risk and the lobbying efforts of particular groups who have raised the profile of this food additive. Knowing that others may have experienced symptoms may be sufficient to put you off, but unless you know you are particularly sensitive to MSG and the many foods that naturally contain glutamates, you can safely eat it.

Use: As a flavour enhancer in savoury products.

Likely products: Soups; sauces; sausages; savoury snacks such as Chicken and Mushroom Pot Noodle, Quavers and Monster Munch.

Food scares: In 1968 with Chinese Restaurant Syndrome – see above.

Should you be scared of them? No.

ADI (Acceptable Daily Intake): Not specified.

E626
Guanylic acid (Flavour enhancers)

E628
Dipotassium guanylate

E629
Calcium guanylate

E630
Inosinic acid

E632
Dipotassium inosinate

E633
Calcium inosinate

Although technically these are permitted, none is produced or actually used in the food industry.

Use: Could be used as flavour enhancers, but E627 and E631 are used instead.

Likely products: None.

Should you be scared of them? No.

ADI (Acceptable Daily Intake): Not specified.

E627
Disodium 5'-guanylate, including disodium guanosine 5'monophosphate (GMP) (Flavour enhancer)

Made from yeast and the fermentation of sugars, this is used to improve the savoury taste of foods, and seasonings, by suppressing or masking flavours that are overly predominant.

Use: This is a flavour enhancer.
Likely products: Sauces, soups and seasonings. Processed meats, poultry and seafood.
Should you be scared of it? No.
ADI (Acceptable Daily Intake): Not specified.

E631
Disodium inosinate; Disodium insoine 5-monophosphate (IMP) (Flavour enhancer)

Made from yeast, or by fermenting sugar, these flavour enhancers are used in savoury products to increase the intensity of the flavour, which is usually released on chewing.

Use: As a flavour enhancer often in conjunction with one of the glutamates.
Likely products: Savoury dishes such as soups, instant noodles, sauces, processed meat and seafood.
Should you be scared of it? No.
ADI (Acceptable Daily Intake): None set.

E634 🍎
Calcium 5 –ribonucleotides

E635 🍎
Disodium5-ribonucleotides
(Flavour enhancers)

Made synthetically, these two flavour enhancers are sometimes used in conjunction with MSG to intensify flavour, though E634 is rarely used in Europe.

Use: As a flavour enhancer.

Likely products: Miso, processed meat and poultry such as Peperami; fish and seafood; yeast extract; cheese- and tomato-based foods. Used in Wotsits Really Cheesy, Quavers and Frazzles.

Should you be scared of them? No, if you suffer from gout it may be prudent to avoid these but there is no strong evidence for this, particularly since they are limited to half a gram per kilogram of seasonings.

ADI (Acceptable Daily Intake): None set.

E640 🍎
Glycine (Browning agent, antioxidant, preservative)

This is a naturally occurring amino acid – a constituent of protein and is a normal part of the diet. It is sweet in taste and combines with sugars to brown foods. It may also be synthesized from gelatine.

Use: Mainly used as a browning and seasoning agent, it is also used for its preservative and antioxidant properties.

Likely products: Meats, baked goods such as cakes and pies, and in dietetic foods.

Should you be scared of it? No, but you may want to avoid if you are vegetarian.

ADI (Acceptable Daily Intake): Present uses are safe and not of toxicological concern.

E650
Zinc acetate (Flavour enhancer)

Zinc acetate is often found in dietary supplements and throat lozenges as zinc supplementation as it is thought to reduce the severity of common colds. In the food industry its flavour-enhancing properties are used.

Use: Another flavour enhancer which is astringent in taste and may be used to intensify bitterness.
Likely products: Dietary supplements and chewing gum.
Nutritional/medical benefits: Zinc is an essential mineral, but the amount consumed as a flavour enhancer is unlikely to have much dietary impact.
Should you be scared of it? No.
ADI (Acceptable Daily Intake): None set.

E900
Dimethyl polysioxane; Silicone; Silicone oil (Anti-foaming agent)

You are probably more familiar with silicone in your furniture polish than in foods, but it is permitted in tiny quantities for use as an anti-foaming agent in liquids.

Use: As an antifoaming agent, to prevent jam boiling over and fizzy drinks frothing up during bottling or canning.
Likely products: Jams; carbonated and other soft drinks, some oil used by caterers.
Should you be scared of it? No.
ADI (Acceptable Daily Intake): 0–1.5 mg/kg body weight.

E901
Beeswax (Glazing agent)

Natural beeswax can be used to glaze sweets and jellies, and may also be mixed with other waxes.

Use: As a glaze.
Source: Made from honeycomb.
Likely products: Sweets, jellies, baked goods and dietary supplements.
Should you be scared of it? No. There are no clinical studies that show any negative effects.
ADI (Acceptable Daily Intake): Present uses are safe and not of toxicological concern, based on long history of use of this and unlikely exposure of more than tiny amounts.

E902
Candelilla wax (Glazing agent)

A natural wax extracted from the candelilla plant, *Euphorbia antisphilitica* Zucc.

Use: To glaze confectionery and fruit that is being stored, as it repels water.
Source: Made from the candelilla plant.
Likely products: Chewing gum, confectionery and fruit.
Should you be scared of it? No.
ADI (Acceptable Daily Intake): Present uses are safe and not of toxicological concern.

E903
Carnauba wax (Glazing agent)

This wax is made from the palm known as *Copernicia prunifera*.

Use: As a glazing agent on sweets or to reduce water loss during storage on fruit.
Likely products: Glazed sweets and chocolate candy, some fruit and dietary supplements.

Should you be scared of it? No. There are no clinical studies to show any negative effects.

ADI (Acceptable Daily Intake): 0–7 mg/kg body weight.

E904
Shellac (Colouring, glazing agent)

Shellac has been around for 3,000 years and is in active use across the world for various purposes. In India, a whole industry has grown up around the production of shellac, and I've seen street-jewellers making bangles and necklaces from it in Rajasthan. It's also the glaze used to give sweets like Skittles their shiny surface. The female lac beetle sucks the sap of the kursum tree and uses it to secrete this resin, forming a cocoon around itself. When lots of these tiny bugs are gathered in one place by infesting the tree, the amount of resin they secrete can be substantial. It is harvested by being knocked off the tree in clumps, and is then refined to clean and process it. Most gramophone records used to be made out of shellac until vinyl took over. Vegetarians may want to think twice about it, as, although its collection does not involve killing the bug, they sometimes get caught up in it. It is very widely used in other industries from French polishing to bike handlebar tape.

Use: Naturally coloured in different shades, it is used to coat confectionery, some biscuits and gums with a glaze and may be used with other glazing agents.

Likely products: Sweets, gums and coated chocolate confectionery.

Should you be scared of it? No. There are no clinical studies to show any negative effects.

ADI (Acceptable Daily Intake): Present uses are safe and not of toxicological concern.

E905
Microcrystalline wax (Coating agent)

This is not a 'natural' wax as the other waxes described, as it is made from by-products of the petroleum industry..

Use: It is used to prevent chewing gum sticking together.
Likely products: Chewing gum.
Should you be scared of it? No.
ADI (Acceptable Daily Intake): 0–20 mg/kg body weight

E912
Montan acid esters (Glazing agent)

This wax is made from a substance called lignite or brown coal and is used mostly in shoe polish and paint as it is scuff-resistant. It is only permitted to be used on the surface of exotic and citrus fruit, but since it tastes nasty it is not (thankfully) widely used.

Use: As a glaze.
Likely products: Some fruits.
Should you be scared of it? No.
ADI (Acceptable Daily Intake): None set.

E914
Oxidised polyethylene wax (Glazing agent)

Made from polyethylene, this is used to coat fruit after washing to protect against moisture loss in storage.

Use: As an glazing agent.
Likely products: Fresh citrus and exotic fruit.
Should you be scared of it? No.
ADI (Acceptable Daily Intake): None set.

E920 🍎 🧍

L-cysteine hydrochloride (Flour improver)

Cysteine is an amino acid made by the liver. The hydrochloride version is sometimes used in dietary supplements. Although synthetic versions are now made, the source of this additive is usually duck feathers or (*outside the EU*) human hair (see page 37), so vegetarians beware! It may also interfere with insulin so diabetics may wish to avoid it.

Use: E920 is used to improve flour used in bread and pizza making.
Likely products: Pizza bases and burger buns, dietary supplements.
Should you be scared of it? No, as it is no longer legally sourced from human hair in EU.
ADI (Acceptable Daily Intake): None set.

E927b

Carbamide (Acidity regulator)

Made synthetically from ammonia and carbon dioxide, carbamide (or urea) is a permitted additive in sugar-free chewing gum where it decreases the acidity in the mouth after eating. It is present naturally in the body as it carries waste protein through the kidneys in the production of urine.

Use: To reduce acidity. It can be used at up to 3% by weight in chewing gum, but is not permitted in other products.
Likely products: Sugar-free chewing gum.
Nutritional/medical benefits: Helps reduce the risk of dental cavities when you chew sugar-free chewing gum.
Should you be scared of it? No.
ADI (Acceptable Daily Intake): Current levels are acceptable.

E938 🍎

Argon (Preservative)

Argon is a natural gas found in the atmosphere. It can be captured and processed for use in packaging to increase shelf life, as food spoilage organisms will be deprived of oxygen for growth.

Use: For use in 'modified atmosphere' packaging to lengthen shelf life.
Source: From the atmosphere where it is dried, filtered and compressed.
Likely products: Ready-to-eat meals, including pizzas; cooked meats; wine and snacks.
Should you be scared of it? No.
ADI (Acceptable Daily Intake): None set.

E939 🍎

Helium (Preservative)

In theory, helium could be used as a food additive but it is not currently used in the food industry.

E941 🍎
Nitrogen (Preservative)

Nitrogen is present in the air around us; in fact it makes up 78.1% of the atmosphere. Its use in foods is to displace oxygen, which otherwise allows food spoilage organisms to multiply. So it effectively increases shelf life. Nitrogen, or a mix of nitrogen and carbon dioxide, is frequently used in modified atmosphere packaging. Liquid nitrogen has applications in freezing and chilling foods, and the dairy industry uses nitrogen in whipping desserts and creams.

Use: Used in modified atmosphere packaging to extend shelf life.
Likely products: Part-baked breads and doughs; dried foods such as milk and potato powder; snacks and dairy desserts.
Should you be scared of it? No.
ADI (Acceptable Daily Intake): 'No ADI necessary' according to JECFA.

E942
Nitrous oxide (Propellant)

Nitrous oxide or laughing gas is made from nitrogen-based compounds and used as a propellant in 'squirty creams', i.e. canned aerosol cream.

Use: Mostly used in dairy products, where it prevents the damage of fat due to oxygen. Also used as a propellant in aerosol creams. Because nitrous oxide is not stable, the whipped cream can become liquid again unless used immediately.
Likely products: Aerosol-based creams, such as Squirty Real Dairy Cream.
Nutritional/medical benefits: Has long been used as an anaesthetic and, on its discovery in 1799, was used as a recreational drug at parties. Although this still persists, there are dangers from inhaling nitrous oxide straight from canister, so don't try it!
Should you be scared of it? No. There are no clinical studies that show any negative effects.
ADI (Acceptable Daily Intake): Current levels are acceptable as a propellant.

E943a
Butane

E943b
Iso-butane

E944
Propane (Propellants)

These three gases are made from natural gas and are permitted propellants in oil sprays and water-based emulsion sprays for professional use only. This means that unless you work in the food industry you are unlikely to come across them in foods.

Use: As a propellant.
Likely products: Vegetable oil pan sprays and water-based emulsion sprays.
Should you be scared of them? No.
ADI (Acceptable Daily Intake): None allocated.

E948 🍎
Oxygen (Preservative)

In most packaging, oxygen is excluded because it allows bacteria and other food spoilage organisms to grow. However, for some foods a small amount of oxygen is used along with carbon dioxide. This is the case with cuts of red meat, which benefit in colour from the presence of a small amount of oxygen – being red rather than purplish. Some seafood packaging also uses oxygen to prevent the growth of *Clostridium botulinum*, which favours oxygen-free conditions. Lastly, controlled amounts of oxygen are added to packs of produce, such as prepared lettuce and salad bags, which continue to respire after cutting and packaging.

Use: In packaging to increase the shelf life of specific foodstuffs.
Likely products: Prepared salad leaves; fresh meat; fish and seafood.
Should you be scared of it? No.
ADI (Acceptable Daily Intake): None set.

E949
Hydrogen (Hydrogenator)

A gas made from petroleum used in the production of fats from oils through a process called hydrogenation. It may also be used in packaging.

Use: In the production of solid fats from liquid oils.
Source: Made by heating gas or hydrocarbon fuels at high temperatures.
Likely products: The gas is only present during the production process of fats and spreads, not in the end product.
Should you be scared of it? No.
ADI (Acceptable Daily Intake): None set.

E950
Acesulfame K; Acesulfame potassium (Sweetener)

A synthetic calorie-free sweetener that is 180–200 times sweeter than ordinary sugar.

Use: Used both a sweetener and a flavour enhancer (although it has a slightly bitter taste), often in conjunction with other sweeteners, especially E951 Aspartame.
Likely products: Used in a huge range of foods in which an intense sweetener is required, notably beverages such as Cadbury's Highlights Chocolate Drinks; yoghurts; ice cream and other dairy products; desserts; confectionery and chewing gum.
Food scares: There was at one time wide concern that this had carcinogenic properties, but this was never adequately proven. It is now approved by both the USDA and the EU.
Nutritional/medical benefits: Does not contribute to tooth decay and is safe for diabetics. It is useful for people who want to reduce their calorie intake, and may help combat obesity.
Should you be scared of it? No.
ADI (Acceptable Daily Intake): 0–15 mg/kg body weight.

E951
Aspartame (Sweetener)

A synthetic nutritive sweetener composed of two amino acids.

Use: Another intense sweetener 200 times sweeter than ordinary sugar, this also serves as a flavour enhancer, especially with fruit. It is often used in conjunction with other sweeteners, especially E950 acesulfame K.

Likely products: Like acesulfame K, this is used in a huge range of foods in which an intense sweetener is required, notably liquid and dried beverages; yoghurts; ice cream and other dairy products; desserts; gelatins; confectionery and chewing gum.

Food scares: When aspartame breaks down in the body, one of the products is the natural amino acid phenylalanine, which can be dangerous for those born with a rare genetic disease phenylketonuria, which does not allow their bodies to metabolize phenylalanine, so in many countries including the UK and the USA, products containing aspartame must carry a warning on this subject on their packaging. Soon after aspartame's discovery in 1965, two activists concerned about the effects of food additives claimed that the safety tests duly conducted on the chemical had indicated that it might cause cancer in rats. As a result it was not approved by the USFDA for many years and it was not until 1983, after much debate and reexamination of those early test results and further studies, that they removed all restrictions from its use. It gained EU-wide approval in 1994. In 1999, FDA officials described the safety of aspartame as 'clear cut' and stated that the product is 'one of the most thoroughly tested and studied food additives the agency has ever approved'. This has not prevented it remaining one of the leading subjects of unsubstantiated concerns about food additives.

Nutritional/medical benefits: Does not contribute to tooth decay and is safe for diabetics. It is useful for people who want to reduce their calorie intake, and may help combat obesity.

Should you be scared of it? No, but note the above.

ADI (Acceptable Daily Intake): 0–40 mg/kg body weight.

E952
Cyclamic acid and its Na and Ca salts (Sweetener)

Cyclamic acid is a synthetic sweetener and its sodium and calcium salts are the forms in which it is used commercially. Cyclamates are about 30 times sweeter than ordinary sugar.

Use: A potent low-calorie sweetener, it is often used in conjunction with other sweeteners, such as saccharin, aspartame and acesulfame K. It is particularly compatible with citrus flavours.

Likely products: Mostly soft drinks and table-top sweeteners.

Food scares: In 1958, twenty-one years after its invention at the University of Illinois, cyclamate was designated GRAS (Generally Recognized as Safe) in the USA. In the late 1960s, US studies first of all linked cyclamates with cancer and later with testicular atrophy. In 1969 the USFDA banned its sale and the UK did the same a year later. Its licensed manufacturer, Abbott Laboratories has petitioned the USFDA several times since to lift its ban, but it remains banned in the USA, although the FDA has stated that a review of all available evidence does not implicate cyclamate as a carcinogen in mice or rats. It is, however, now approved for use in Canada, the UK and over 50 other countries.

Nutritional/medical benefits: Does not contribute to tooth decay and is safe for diabetics. It is useful for people who want to reduce their calorie intake, and may help combat obesity.

Should you be scared of it? No, but note the above.

ADI (Acceptable Daily Intake): 0–7 mg/kg body weight.

E953
Isomalt (Sweetener)

A natural 'sugar alcohol' derived from beetroots, the commercial additive is made from ordinary sugar (sucrose).

Use: A low-calorie sweetener that also provides bulk and texture. It also dissolves slowly, so sweets containing it last longer in the mouth.

Likely products: Baked products and confectionery; chewing gum; chocolate products and ice cream.

Food scares: As E421.

Nutritional/medical benefits: Unlike other sugars, does not encourage tooth decay. It is useful for people who want to reduce their calorie intake, and may help combat obesity,

Should you be scared of it? No, but note the above.

ADI (Acceptable Daily Intake): Not specified.

E954
Saccharin and its Na, K and Ca salts (Sweetener)

One of the earliest of the artificial sweeteners, saccharin has been made from petroleum for over a hundred years and became an important product during the First World War's sugar shortages.

Use: An intense sweetener, 450 times sweeter than ordinary sugar, it is used to replace sugar in reduced-calorie products. However, it has a bitter metallic aftertaste, so is nowadays more usually used in combination with other sweeteners. As saccharin itself is not water-soluble, the form used as a sweetener is mostly its sodium salt (or the calcium salt for those on low-sodium diets).

Likely products: Low- or reduced-calorie products, such as soft drinks; jams; baked goods; canned fruit; desserts and salad dressings.

Food scares: Like many food additives in the 1960s and 1970s, saccharin was found in various studies to be linked to an increased rate of cancer in rats. In response, Canada banned it and the USFDA proposed a ban, but there was an outcry from the public, diabetics in particular, as it was at that time the only artificial sweetener available in the USA. As a result the ban was set aside in favour of a warning label. Since then there have been more studies and continuous debate on their significance. In 2000, The U.S. National Institute of Environmental Health Sciences recommended that saccharin be removed from the list of known or suspected human carcinogens on the grounds that the previously observed link appears to be due to the way that rats metabolize sodium, and bladder cancer which cannot be replicated in other mammals has also been observed with rat consumption of other sodium salts such as sodium citrate and bicarbonate. In 1991, the FDA formally withdrew its 1977 proposal to ban the use of saccharin, and in 2000, the US Congress repealed the law requiring saccharin products to carry health-warning labels.

Nutritional/medical benefits: Does not contribute to tooth decay and is safe for diabetics. It is useful for people who want to reduce their calorie intake, and may help combat obesity.

Should you be scared of it? No.

ADI (Acceptable Daily Intake): 0–5 mg/kg body weight.

E955

Sucralose (Sweetener)

A zero-calorie intense synthetic sweetener made from sugar.

Use: About 600 times sweeter than sugar, this has the abilities to be highly soluble in water, even at low temperatures, and to withstand high temperature food processing and long-term storage.

Likely products: Beverages and soft drinks; canned fruit; baked goods; desserts and confectionery.

Should you be scared of it? No.

Nutritional/medical benefits: Does not contribute to tooth decay and is safe for diabetics. It is useful for people who want to reduce their calorie intake, and may help combat obesity.

ADI (Acceptable Daily Intake): 0–15 mg/kg body weight.

E957
Thaumatin (Sweetener)

A naturally sweet mixture of proteins obtained from the katemfe fruit of a tree native to the African green belt, *Thaumatoccus danielli*.

Use: About 2,500 times sweeter than sugar, this is used at very low levels for its flavouring properties as it can mask unpleasant tastes and improve both the flavour and mouthfeel of a wide range of products.

Likely products: Beverages; ice cream; desserts; chewing gum and confectionery.

Nutritional/medical benefits: Does not contribute to tooth decay and is safe for diabetics. It is useful for people who want to reduce their calorie intake, and may help combat obesity.

Should you be scared of it? No.

ADI (Acceptable Daily Intake): Not specified.

E959
Neohesperidine DC (Sweetener)

An intense sweetener obtained as a by-product of the processing of bitter oranges.

Use: About 1,000–1,800 times sweeter than sugar, it is used in very small amounts to enhance sweet taste and fruit flavour, and to increase pleasant mouthfeel. It has a distinctive liquorice taste so is rarely used on its own and is noted for its synergy with many other sweeteners.

Likely products: Chewing gum; ketchup; mayonnaise; alcoholic beverages; soft drinks; dairy products; ice cream and desserts.

Food scares: Can cause nausea and migraine at high doses.

Nutritional/medical benefits: Does not contribute to tooth decay and is safe for diabetics to add. It is useful for people who want to reduce their calorie intake, and may help combat obesity.

Should you be scared of it? No, but note the above.

ADI (Acceptable Daily Intake): 0–5 mg/kg body weight.

E962
Salt of aspartame-acesulfame (Sweetener)

A synthetic intense sweetener obtained by heating a mixture of aspartame and acesulfame K in an acidic medium.

Use: Used in place of aspartame as it is more stable.
Likely products: Non-alcoholic beverages; dairy products; confectionery; chewing gum and table-top sweeteners.
Food scares: See E950 and E951.
Nutritional/medical benefits: Does not contribute to tooth decay and is safe for diabetics. It is useful for people who want to reduce their calorie intake, and may help combat obesity,
Should you be scared of it? No, but see the above.
ADI (Acceptable Daily Intake): None allocated.

E965
(i) Maltitol; (ii) Maltitol syrup (Sweetener)

Synthetic nutritive sweeteners. Maltitol is made from maltose and is 90% as sweet as sugar, while the syrup is 60–85%.

Use: It replaces sugar and glucose syrups for bulk, texture and sweetness. Maltitol's crystalline structure helps give a crunchy coating to products like sugar-free chewing gum.
Likely products: Sugar-free confectionery products such as chewing gum, chocolates, pastilles, gums and both hard and soft sweets; ice cream.
Food scares: As E421.
Nutritional/medical benefits: It does not contribute to tooth decay or cause increase in blood glucose, so is suitable for diabetics. Some recent studies seem to indicate that it can have a beneficial effect on colonic and rectal cancers.
Should you be scared of it? No, but note the above.
ADI (Acceptable Daily Intake): Not specified.

E966
Lactitol (Sweetener)

Another 'sugar alcohol' made from whey, the by-product of cheese making and processed dairy foods, which can be rich in lactose (milk sugar).

Use: Bulk sweetener in sugar-free, sugar-reduced and low-calorie foods.

Natural version: Milk.

Likely products: 'No-added sugar', 'energy-reduced', 'tooth-friendly' or dietetic foods, such as baked goods, confectionery, ice cream, chewing gum and jams.

Food scares: Excessive consumption can cause bloating and flatulence, and have a laxative effect on those few people intolerant to it. Lactose intolerance is particularly prevalent.

Nutritional/medical benefits: It does not contribute to tooth decay or cause increase in blood glucose, so is suitable for diabetics. Promotes colon health as a prebiotic in many types of functional foods, such as yoghurts.

Should you be scared of it? No, but note the above.

ADI (Acceptable Daily Intake): Not specified.

E967
Xylitol (Sweetener)

A 'sugar alcohol' used as a natural sugar substitute. It is found in the fibres of many trees, fruits and vegetables, including various berries, corn husks, oats, and mushrooms. Xylitol is roughly as sweet as sucrose with only two-thirds the food energy.

Use: As a non-fermentable low-calorie bulk sweetener and to mask other ingredients.

Source: Birch, raspberries, plums and corn.

Likely products: Some baked goods; confectionery; chewing gum; mints; pastilles and gums.

Food scares: Excessive consumption can cause bloating and flatulence, and have a laxative effect on those few people intolerant to it.

Nutritional/medical benefits: Used in diabetic foods as it does not affect blood glucose levels and inhibits oral bacteria and dental caries, so used in 'tooth-friendly' sweets. It is useful for people who want to reduce their calorie intake, and may help combat obesity. Studies have shown that chewing gum containing it help prevent ear infections (the chewing and swallowing assists with clearing the middle ear while the xylitol prevents the growth of bacteria in the tubes that connect the nose and ear. It also has potential as a treatment for osteoporosis. A group of finnish researchers has found that dietary xylitol prevents weakening of bones in laboratory rats, and actually improves bone density. Another recent report suggests that it may help control oral infections of Candida yeast (while glucose and sucrose may encourage them).

Should you be scared of it? No, but note the above.

ADI (Acceptable Daily Intake): Not specified.

E968
Erythritol (Sweetener)

A natural sugar alcohol obtained from fruits and fermented foods, and also made from glucose. It is as sweet as ordinary sugar but has practically no calorific content.

Use: As well as acting as a sweetener, it is used as flavour enhancer, stabilizer, thickener and bulking agent.

Likely products: Confectionery; desserts; frozen fish and seafood and liqueurs.

Food scares: Excessive consumption can cause bloating and flatulence, and have a laxative effect on those few people intolerant to it, but needs to be at even higher dose than other sweeteners to produce these effects.

Nutritional/medical benefits: Does not contribute to tooth decay and is safe for diabetics. It is useful for people who want to reduce their calorie intake, and may help combat obesity.

Should you be scared of it? No, but see above.

ADI (Acceptable Daily Intake): Not specified.

E999
Quillaia extract (Foaming agent)

This comes from the inner bark of the *Quillaia saponaria* or Molina tree, from where it is extracted and made into a powder. It apparently provides a stable foam, so is used in drinks such as cream soda where a 'head' is desirable.

Use: As a foaming agent.
Likely products: Cream soda and ginger beer.
Should you be scared of it? No.
ADI (Acceptable Daily Intake): None set.

E1103 🍎 🚶
Invertase (Enzyme)

Invertase is actually a biologically active compound called an enzyme, which breaks down sugars. In humans it is naturally found in the mouth. It is made industrially from yeasts and is essential in the production of golden syrup or other 'invert syrups'.

Use: As an enzyme to help change sugar into syrup.
Likely products: In golden syrup and confectionery that has liquid centres.
Should you be scared of it? No.
ADI (Acceptable Daily Intake): Current levels are acceptable.

E1105 🍎 🚶
Lysozyme (Preservative)

A natural enzyme extracted from hens' egg albumen.

Use: In place of nitrates.
Natural version: Eggs; also found in tears, saliva, blood and (human) milk.
Likely products: Cheeses, such as the Italian hard cheese (and rival to Parmesan) Grana Padano.
Nutritional/medical benefits: Added to infants' milk formula to boost the immune system.

Should you be scared of it? No.
ADI (Acceptable Daily Intake): Current levels are acceptable.

E1200 🍎
Polydextrose (Bulking agent, thickener, sugar replacement, texturizer)

Made from glucose in a complex process, this additive is commonly used in foods as a bulking agent, mainly to replace sugars in dietetically designed products. It is sold commercially as Litesse (among other trade names), and since it is not metabolized in the same way as most carbohydrates, it is often used in low-carb or low-GI (glycaemic index) foods. The use of polydextrose is not restricted to carbohydrate-based foods, as it can also be used in foods containing fat, where it replicates the mouth-feel of fat. It also extends shelf life in baked foods, as it slows down the loss of moisture.

Use: As a bulking agent, thickener and to prevent moisture loss. It may also be used as a prebiotic in foods (something which beneficial probiotic bacteria use to grow.)

Likely products: Dietetic products labelled 'low-GI', 'low-carb' or 'reduced energy (calorie)', such as chocolate, confectionery, frozen desserts, baked goods, fruit fillings and spreads, and surimi.

Nutritional/medical benefits: Indirectly it helps to create low-calorie foods, so may help you combat obesity if you manage to lose weight on a calorie-controlled diet.

Should you be scared of it? No.

ADI (Acceptable Daily Intake): None set.

E1201
Polyvinylpyrrolidone (PVP)

E1202
Polyvinylpolypyrrolidone (PVPP)
(Water absorbers)

These are synthetic water-absorbent but water-insoluble additives used in tablets such as dietary supplements. Their ability to absorb water assists with the breakdown of the tablet in the gut.

Use: Found in food supplement tablets to help them break down and in food sweetener preparations. They are also used in winemaking for the fining (clarification) of white wine, but are no longer present by time the wine is sold.

Likely products: Dietary supplements.

Should you be scared of it? No.

ADI (Acceptable Daily Intake): 0–50 mg/kg body weight.

E1204
Pullulan (Coating agent)

If you like those breath-freshening strips that melt on the tongue you will be enjoying the benefits of E1204. Made using a fungus to ferment a type of starch, then sterilised and further processed, it is a type of carbohydrate – a hydrolyzed starch that is both flexible and soluble, hence its use as a food-grade film.

Use: Its use is permitted in breath-freshening sweets and films or as a capsule coating.

Likely products: Breath-freshening sweets and films, and dietary supplements.

Nutritional/medical benefits: If you suffer from halitosis these products may be of assistance.

Should you be scared of it? No. A recent study used Pullulan as a source of fibre and it was well tolerated by the subjects in the study.

ADI (Acceptable Daily Intake): Not specified.

E1404
Oxidised starch (Thickening agent, stabilizer)
Oxidised starches are starches that have been treated to change their texture and function. They tend to be used in confectionery for gums and lozenges. Some are used in the batter industry as they make the batter stick more readily to the food it is covering.

Use: Used in battered foods, such as fish, poultry, meat and vegetables. Also used in gums.
Likely products: Battered fish; poultry; meat; vegetables; gums and lozenges.
Food scares: None.
Should you be scared of it? No.
ADI (Acceptable Daily Intake): None set.

E1410
Monostarch phosphate

E1412
Distarch Phosphate

E1413
Phosphated distarch phosphate

E1414
Acetylated distarch phosphate

E1420
Acetylated starches

E1422
Acetylated distarch adipate

E1440
Hydroxyl propyl starch

E1442
Hydroxy propyl distarch phosphate

E1450
starch sodium octenylatssuccinate

E1451
Acetlyated oxidised starch
(Thickening agents, emulsifiers, stabilisers)

These are all common starches that have been modified by chemical treatment. Modifying the starch granule means it becomes more stable when subjected to heat, acid and other conditions, so that food is less likely to separate out, and will remain at the desired consistency or texture in storage. Different qualities are required for different foodstuffs hence the range of different types. Some are designed to be used at low temperatures, others provide a good 'mouth feel' and yet others influence the temperature or speed at which a starch solution (think of making white sauce) may thicken.

Use: As thickening agents, emulsifiers and stabilizers.

Likely products: E1410 Frozen gravy and pie fillings; salad dressings and pudding mixes.

E1412 Sauces and dressings; dry mix desserts and some baked goods.

E1413 Sauces, frozen gravies and pie fillings.

E1414 Soups; sauces; dairy products and fruit pie fillings.

E1420 Batters and bread coatings; cereals and confectionery, snacks.

E1422 Gravy; soups; salad dressings and mayonnaise; fillings; yoghurt drinks such as Bio Green Originals.

E1440 Meat, drinks and dietetic products.

E1442 Gravy; soup; sauces; salad dressings and mayonnaise; fillings; fruit preparations; dairy products, meats and meat substitutes.

E1450 Sauces, mayonnaise and salad dressings; spray-dried flavours.

E1451 Soft sugar confectionery.

Food Scares: None. Nothing to do with genetically modified starches or other genetically modified foods.

Should you be scared of them? No. There are no clinical studies that show any negative effects.

ADI (Acceptable Daily Intake): Not specified.

E1452
Starch aluminium octenyl succinate
(Modified starch, coating agent)

This is a synthetic starch powder that prevents dry goods from sticking together.

Use: Used in powders, such as in vitamin capsules or other dietary supplements.
Likely products: Micro-encapsulated vitamins.
Should you be scared of it? No.
ADI (Acceptable Daily Intake): None set.

E1505
Triethyl citrate (Foaming agent, stabilizer)

Made from a reaction between citric acid (E330) and ethanol (alcohol), this is a little-used additive as it is only permitted in dehydrated egg white and a few specific flavourings.

Use: In dried egg white it speeds up the creation of foam on whipping.
Likely products: Dried egg white and food containing added flavours.
Should you be scared of it? No.
ADI (Acceptable Daily Intake): 0–2 mg/kg body weight.

E1517

Glyceryl diacetate; diacetin (Flavour carrier)

Flavours often need to be dissolved in a simple, stable, neutral substance so they can be added to foodstuffs. These are called carrier solvents and this compound, made from glycerol, is one of them.

Use: As a flavour carrier.
Likely products: A limited range of foods with added flavours.
Should you be scared of it? No.
ADI (Acceptable Daily Intake): Not specified.

E1518

Glyceryl triacetate (Lubricant, flavouring)

This lubricant, made from glycerol, is used almost entirely in chewing gum, although it is also permitted in flavourings.

Use: As a lubricant in chewing gum.
Likely products: Chewing gum.
Should you be scared of it? No.
ADI (Acceptable Daily Intake): Not specified.

E1520
Propane-1,2 diol; propylene glycol
(Anti-caking agent, emulsifier, thickener, stabilizer, flavour carrier)

The synthetic compound propylene glycol, as it is more frequently known, has a vast array of functions in foods and is also used extensively in non-food products such as cosmetic moisturizers and paint balls. It is strictly controlled in the types of foods and quantities that are permitted, and is easily metabolized by the body.

Use: There are various uses: in general it is used to help retain moisture, but it is specifically used as an anti-caking agent to stop dry foods from sticking together; as an emulsifier to prevent mixtures containing water and oil from separating, and also as a thickener and stabilizer and a flavour carrier.

Likely products: A wide range of foods and drinks.

Should you be scared of it? No.

ADI (Acceptable Daily Intake): 0–25 mg/kg body weight.

Appendices

i—Organic Es

There are certain E numbers allowed for use in the production of processed organic foods, these are:

E 153 Vegetable carbon
E 160b Annatto, Bixin, Norbixin
E 170 Calcium carbonate
E 220 Sulphur dioxide
E 224 Potassium metabisulphite
E 270 Lactic acid
E 290 Carbon dioxide
E 296 Malic acid
E 300 Ascorbic acid
E 301 Sodium ascorbate
E 306 Tocopherol-rich extract
E 322 Lecithins
E 325 Sodium lactate
E 330 Citric acid
E 331 Sodium citrates
E 333 Calcium citrates
E 334 Tartaric acid
E 335 Sodium tartrates
E 336 Potassium tartrates
E 341 Calcium phosphates
E 400 Alginic acid
E 401 Sodium alginate
E 402 Potassium alginate
E 406 Agar
E 407 Carrageenan
E 410 Locust bean gum
E 412 Guar gum
E 414 Arabic gum
E 415 Xanthan gum
E 422 Glycerol
E 440 Pectin

E 464 Hydroxypropyl methyl cellulose
E 500 Sodium carbonates
E 501 Potassium carbonates
E 503 Ammonium carbonates
E 504 Magnesium carbonates
E 509 Calcium chloride
E 516 Calcium sulphate
E 524 Sodium hydroxide
E 551 Silicon dioxide
E 553b Talc
E 938 Argon
E 939 Helium
E 941 Nitrogen
E 948 Oxygen

ii—Halal and kosher Es

Certification of these foods is on a food-by-food basis, so there is generally no central list of accepted additives. Because some foods may contain additives that may be derived from plants or animals in origin, the foods themselves have to be certified on the basis of the exact ingredients and additives they contain.

A list of E numbers that derive from animal origins are listed below, however this does not mean that all other additives are necessarily Halal or kosher – animal origin cannot be excluded – only the producer and/or ingredient supplier is able to provide this information.

E numbers that derive from animal origin and may want to be avoided by those who are following Halal and kosher diets include:

E120 Cochineal; Carminic acid; Carmines
E322 Lecithins
E422 Ammonium phosphatides
E430 Polyoxyethylene (8) stearate
E431 Polyoxyethylene (40) stearate
E432 Polyoxyethylene sorbitan monolaurate; Polysorbate 20
E433 Polyoxyethylene sorbitan mono-oleate; Polysorbate 80
E434 Polyoxyethylene sorbitan monopalmitate; Polysorbate 40
E435 Polyoxyethylene sorbitan monostearate; Polysorbate 60
E436 Polyoxyethylene sorbitan tristearate; Polysorbate 65
E470 Sodium, potassium and calcium salts of fatty acids
E471 Mono- and diglycerides of fatty acids
E472a Acetic acid esters of mono- and diglycerides of fatty acids
E472b Lactic acid esters of mono- and diglycerides of fatty acids
E472c Citric acid esters of mono- and diglycerides of fatty acids
E472d Tartaric acid esters of mono- and diglycerides of fatty acids
E472e Mono-and diacetyltartaric acid esters of mono- and diglycerides of fatty acids
E472f Mixed acetic and tartaric acid esters of mono- and diglycerides of fatty acids
E473 Sucrose esters of fatty acids
E474 Sucroglycerides

E475 Polyglycerol esters of fatty acids
E477 Propane-1,2-diol esters of fatty acids
E478 Lactylated fatty acid esters of glycerol and propane-1
E479b Thermally oxidised soya bean oil interacted with mono and
   diglycerides of fatty acids
E481 Sodium stearoyl-2-lactylate
E482 Calcium stearoyl-2-lactylate
E483 Stearyl tartrate
E484 Stearyl citrate
E491 Sorbitan monostearate
E492 Sorbitan tristearate
E493 Sorbitan monolaurate
E494 Sorbitan monooleate
E495 Sorbitan monopalmitate
E542 Bone phosphate
E570–3 Fatty acids
E626 Guanylic acid
E627 Disodium guanylate
E628 Dipotassium inosolate
E629 Calcium guanylate
E630 Inosinic acid
E631 Disodium inosinate
E632 Dipotassium inosinate
E633 Calcium inosinate
E634 Calcium 5'-ribonucleotides
E635 Disodium 5'ribonucleotides
E640 Glycine and its sodium
E901 Beeswax
E904 Shellac
E913 Lanolin
E920 L-Cysteine
E921 L-cysteine hydrochloride monohydrate
E966 Lactitol
E1000 Cholic acid
E1105 Lysozyme

iii—A–Z of Es

2-Phenylphenol E231
4-Hexylresorcinol E586
Acacia gum E414
Acesulfame K E950
Acetic acid E260
Acetic acid esters of mono- and diglycerides of fatty acids E472a
Acetylated distarch adipate E1422
Acetylated distarch phosphate E1414
Acetylated oxidised starch E1451
Acetylated starch E1420
Adipic acid E355
Agar E406
Alginic acid E400
Allura Red AC E129
Alpha-tocopherol E307
Aluminium E173
Aluminium ammonium sulphate E523
Aluminium calcium silicate E556
Aluminium potassium sulphate E522
Aluminium silicate E559
Aluminium sulphate E520
Aluminium sodium sulphate E521
Amaranth E123
Ammonium alginate E403
Ammonia caramel E150c
Ammonium carbonates E503
Ammonium hydroxide E527
Ammonium phosphatides E442
Ammonium sulphate E517
Annatto E160b
Anthocyanins E163
Argon E938
Ascorbic acid E300
Aspartame E951

Azorubine E122
Beeswax, white and yellow E901
Beetroot Red E162
Bentonite E558
Benzoic acid E210
Beta-apo-8'-carotenal (C30) E160e
Beta-cyclodextrin E459
Betanin E162
Bixin E160b
Biphenyl E230
Borax E285
Boric acid E284
Brilliant Black BN / Black PN E151
Brilliant Blue FCF E133
Brilliant Green BS E142
Brilliant Scarlet 4R E124
Brown FK E154
Brown HT E155
Butane E943a
Butylated hydroxyanisole (BHA) E320
Butylated hydroxytoluene (BHT) E321
C I food black 1 E151
C I food blue 1 E132
C I food blue 2 E133
C I food blue 5 E131
C I food brown 1 E154
C I food brown 3 E155
C I food green 4 E142
C I food orange 5 E160a
C I food orange 6 E160e
C I food orange 7 E160f
C I food orange 8 E161g
C I food red 3 E122
C I food red 7 E124
C I food red 9 E123
C I food red 14 E127
C I food red 17 E129
C I food yellow E104

C I food yellow 3 E110

C I food yellow 4 E102

C I natural green 3 E140

C I natural green 5 E140

C I natural orange E160b

C I natural yellow 3 E100

C I natural yellow 27 E160d

C I pigment white 6 E171

C I pigment white 18 E170

Calcium 5'-ribonucleotides E634

Calcium acetate E263

Calcium alginate E404

Calcium ascorbate E302

Calcium benzoate E213

Calcium bisulphate E227

Calcium carbonate E170

Calcium chloride E509

Calcium citrates E333

Calcium diglutamate E623

Calcium disodium ethylene diamine tetra-acetate; calcium disodium EDTA E385

Calcium ferrocyanide E538

Calcium gluconate E578

Calcium guanylate E629

Calcium hydrogen sulphite E227

Calcium hydroxide E526

Calcium inosinate E633

Calcium lactate E327

Calcium malates E352

Calcium oxide E529

Calcium phosphates E341

Calcium propionate E282

Calcium silicate E552

Calcium sorbate E203

Calcium stearoyl-2-lactylate E482

Calcium sulphate E516

Calcium sulphite E226

Calcium tartrate E354

Candelilla wax E902
Canthaxanthin E161g
Capsanthian; Capsorubin E160c
Carbamide E927b
Carbon dioxide E290
Carboxy methyl cellulose E466
Carboxybenzene E210
Carnauba wax E903
Carob gum E410
Carotenes E160a
Carmines E120
Carminic acid E120
Carmoisine E122
Carrageenan E407
Caustic sulphite caramel E150b
Cellulose E460
Chlorophylls / chlorophyllins E140
Chocolate brown HT E155
Citric acid E330
Citric acid esters of mono- and diglycerides of fatty acids E472c
Cochineal E120
Cochineal Red A E124
Copper complexes of chlorophyll / chlorophyllins E141
Crosslinked sodium carboxy methyl cellulose E468
Curcumin E100
Cyclamic acid and its Na and Ca salts E952
Cystamine E239
D & C red 6 E180
Delta-tocopherol E309
Diferoyl methane E100
Dimethyl dicarbonate / DMDC E242
Dimethylpolysiloxane E900
Diphenyl E230
Diphosphates E450
Dipotassium guanylate E628
Dipotassium inosinate E632
Disodium 5'-ribonucleotides E635
Disodium guanylate E627

Disodium inosinate E631

Distarch phosphate E1412

Dodecyl gallate E312

Dowicide 1 E231

Dowicide A E232

Enocianina E163

Enzymatically hydrolysed carboxy methyl cellulose E469

Erythritol E968

Erythorbic acid E315

Erythrosine E127

Ethyl cellulose E462

Ethyl ester of beta-apo-8'-carotenoic acid (C30) E160f

Ethyl methyl cellulose E465

Ethyl p-hydroxybenzoate E214

F D & C blue 1 E133

F D & C blue 2 E132

F D & C red 2 E123

F D & C red 3 E127

F D & C red 40

F D & C yellow no. 5 E102

F D & C yellow no. 6 E110

Fatty acid esters of ascorbic acid E304

Fatty acids E570

Ferrous gluconate E579

Ferrous lactate E579

Flowers of benzoin E210

Fumaric acid E297

Gamma-tocopherol E308

Gellan gum E418

Gluconic acid E574

Glucono delta-lactone E575

Glutamic acid E620

Glycerol E422

Glycerol esters of wood rosins E445

Glyceryl triacetate E1518

Glycine and its sodium salt E640

Gold E175

Grape colour extract / Grape skin extract E163

Green S E142
Guar gum E412
Guanylic acid E626
Gum arabic E414
Helium E939
Hexamethylene tetramine / Hexamine E239
Hydrochloric acid E507
Hydrogen E949
Hydroxy propyl distarch phosphate E1442
Hydroxyl propyl starch E1440
Hydroxypropyl cellulose E463
Hydroxypropyl methyl cellulose E464
Indigotine / Indigo Carmine E132
Inosinic acid E630
Invertase E1103
Iron oxides and hydroxides E172
Iso-butane E943b
Isomalt E953
Kaolin E559
Karaya gum E416
Kipper Brown E154
Konjac E425
L-Cysteine E920
Lactic acid E270
Lactic acid esters of mono- and diglycerides of fatty acids E472b
Lactitol E966
Lactoflavin E101
Lecithins E322
Litholrubine BK E180
Locust bean gum E410
Lutein E161b
Lycopene E160d
Lysozyme E1105
Magnesium carbonates E504
Magnesium chloride E511
Magnesium chlorophyll E140
Magnesium diglutamate E625
Magnesium hydroxide E528

Magnesium oxide E530
Magnesium phaeophytin E140
Magnesium phosphates E343
Magnesium salts of fatty acids E470b
Magnesium silicate / Magnesium trisilicate E553a
Malic acid E296
Maltitol / Maltitol syrup E965
Mannitol E421
Metatartaric acid E353
Methenamine E239
Methyl cellulose E461
Methyl p-hydroxybenzoate E218
Microcrystalline wax E905
Mixed acetic and tartaric acid esters of mono- and diglycerides of fatty
   acids E472f
Mono- and diglycerides of fatty acids E471
Mono- and diacetyltartaric acid esters of mono- and diglycerides of
   fatty acids E472e
Monoammonium glutamate E624
Monosodium glutamate E621
Monostarch phosphate E1410
Montan acid esters E912
Natamycin E235
Neohesperidine DC E959
New coccine E124
Nisin E234
Nitrogen E941
Nitrous oxide E942
Norbixin E160b
O-phenylphenol E231
Octyl gallate E311
Orange Yellow S E110
Orthophenyl phenol E231
Oxidised polyethylene wax E914
Oxidised starch E1404
Oxygen E948
Paprika extract / Paprika oleoresin E160c
Patent Blue V E131

Pectins E440
Phenylbenzene E230
Phenylcarboxylic acid E210
Phosphated distarch phosphate E1413
Phosphoric acid E338
Pigment rubine E180
Pimaricin E235
Plain caramel E150a
Polydextrose E1200
Polyglycerol esters of fatty acids E475
Polyglycerol polyricinoleate E476
Polyoxyethylene (40) stearate E431
Polyoxyethylene sorbitan monolaurate E432
Polyoxyethylene sorbitan mono-oleate E433
Polyoxyethylene sorbitan monopalmitate E434
Polyoxyethylene sorbitan monostearate E435
Polyoxyethylene sorbitan tristearate E436
Polyphosphates E452
Polysorbate 20 E432
Polysorbate 40 E434
Polysorbate 60 E435
Polysorbate 65 E436
Polysorbate 80 E433
Polyvinylpyrrolidone E1201
Polyvinylpolypyrrolidone E1202
Ponceau 4R E124
Potassium acetate E261
Potassium adipate E357
Potassium alginate E402
Potassium aluminium silicate E555
Potassium benzoate E212
Potassium carbonates E501
Potassium chloride E508
Potassium chlorophyllin E140
Potassium citrates E332
Potassium copper chlorophyllin E141
Potassium ferrocyanide E536
Potassium gluconate E577

Potassium hydrogen sulphite E228
Potassium hydroxide E525
Potassium lactate E326
Potassium malates E351
Potassium metabisulphite E224
Potassium nitrite E249, E252
Potassium phosphates E340
Potassium propionate E283
Potassium sorbate E202
Potassium sulphates E515
Potassium tartrates E336
Processed eucheuma seaweed E407a
Propan-1,2-diol E1520
Propane E944
Propane-1,2-diol alginate E405
Propane-1,2-diol esters of fatty acids E477
Propionic acid E280
Propylene glycol E1520
Propyl gallate E310
Pullulan E1204
Quillaia extract E999
Quinoline yellow E104
Riboflavin / Riboflavin-5'-phosphate E101
Saccharin and its Na, K and Ca salts E954
Salt of aspartame-acesulfame E962
Saltpetre E252
Shellac E904
Silicon dioxide E551
Silver E174
Sodium, potassium and calcium salts of fatty acids E470a
Sodium acetate E262
Sodium adipate E356
Sodium alginate E401
Sodium aluminium phosphate E541
Sodium aluminium silicate E554
Sodium ascorbate E301
Sodium benzoate E211
Sodium bisulphate E222

Sodium carbonates E500
Sodium chlorophyllin E140
Sodium citrates E331
Sodium copper chlorophyllin E141
Sodium erythorbate E316
Sodium ethyl p-hydroxybenzoate E215
Sodium ferrocyanide E535
Sodium gluconate E576
Sodium hydrogen sulphite E222
Sodium hydroxide E524
Sodium lactate E325
Sodium malates E350
Sodium metabisulphite E223
Sodium methyl p-hydroxybenzoate E219
Sodium nitrite E250, E251
Sodium orthophenyl phenol E232
Sodium phosphates E339
Sodium potassium tartrate E337
Sodium propionate E281
Sodium pyrosulphite E223
Sodium stearoyl-2-lactylate E481
Sodium sulphates E514
Sodium sulphite E221
Sodium tartrates E335
Sodium tetraborate E285
Sorbic acid E200
Sorbitan monooleate E494
Sorbitan monopalmitate E495
Sorbitan monostearate E491
Sorbitan tristearate E492
Sorbitol / Sorbitol syrup E420
Soybean hemicellulose E426
Stannous chloride E512
Starch aluminium Octenyl succinate E1452
Starch sodium octenyl succinate E1450
Stearyl tartrate E483
Succinic acid E363
Sucralose E955

Sucroglycerides E474
Sucrose acetate isobutyrate E444
Sucrose esters of fatty acids E473
Sulphite ammonia caramel E150d
Sulphur dioxide E220
Sulphuric acid E513
Sunset Yellow FCF E110
Talc E553b
Tartaric acid E334
Tara gum E417
Tartaric acid esters of mono- and diglycerides of fatty acids E472d
Tartrazine E102
Tennectin E235
Tertiary-butyl hydroquinone (TBHQ) E319
Thaumatin E957
    Thermally oxidised soya bean oil interacted with mono and diglycerides of fatty acids E479b
Titanium dioxide E171
Tocopherols E306
Tragacanth E413
Triacetin E1518
Triammonium citrate E380
Triethyl citrate E1505
Triphosphates E451
Turmeric yellow E100
Vegetable carbon E153
Vitamin B2 E101
Xanthan gum E415
Xylitol E967
Zinc acetate E650

iv—Further reading

– Emerton, Victoria & Choi, Eugenia *Essential Guide to Food Additives*
 third edition Surrey: Leatherhead Publishing, 2008

– Hanssen, Maurice & Marsden, Jill *E for Additives*
 London: Thorsons, 1987

Useful websites

– ELC, the Federation of European Specialty Food Ingredient Industries
 http://www.elc-eu.org/index.html

– European Food Information Council.
 http://www.eufic.org/page/en/show/latest-science-
 news/page/FR/fftid/Food-Additives-Factsheet/

– European Food Standards Agency
 http://www.efsa.europa.eu/

– Food Standards Agency
 http://www.food.gov.uk/safereating/chemsafe/additivesbranch/

– Joint Expert Committee on Food Additives
 http://jecfa.ilsi.org/search.cfm

Index

Main entries for E numbers are listed in order from page 71–213.
If you know the common name see Appendix III to find the E number.

Acknowledgements

This book has been put together at an extraordinary pace by a fantastic team. The most important people were and are my gorgeous wife Georgia Glynn Smith and my delicious little girls Daisy and Poppy who allowed me to disappear off the face of the earth while I wrote it. Thank you for being so kind, brilliant and understanding. Thanks also to the wonderful and tenacious Lorraine Dickey, Lewis Esson, Sybella Marlow, Fiona Wilcock and Jonathan Christie for taking on board such a tricky project, and to Borra, Jan, Emma and Michelle at DML for getting us there.

Huge thanks are due to Janice Hadlow for encouraging me to indulge my culinary obsessions, and to Will Daws, Kari Lia, Cassian Harrison and Kin Shillinglaw for making the TV series 'E numbers – an edible adventure' happen.

This book covers multiple scientific disciplines, and wouldn't have been possible without the help of dozens of people, especially the following: Dr Lisa Ackerley Visiting Professor of Environmental Health, Salford University for help with medical and toxicological facts; Dr Jonty Heaversedge GP for sound medical advice and for the economic ruin of my local cheesemonger with that surprise diagnosis; cancer research specialist Sarah Main for her help understanding preservatives; Ruth Goodman for historical food additives information; Alice Pegg for her extraordinary knowledge of food science and legislation; Dr Kathie Grant from the Health Protection Agency for letting me tickle her botulism; Audrey Deane for running the MSG project; Rob Janes and Mike Batham from the Open University chemistry department; surgeon Mike Edwards for his naval expertise and scurvy advice; Tony Milanowski at Plumpton College for explaining the function of sulphur dioxide; Raymon Row for his good-humoured butchery; my good friend Dr Andrea Sella for helping to blow stuff up; Jun Tanaka, head chef at Pearl Restaurant, for helping us to understand MSG (although he wouldn't dream of using it – simply because for him, its cheating!); plastic surgeon Mike Comins at the Hans Place practice for making something extraordinarily scary a lot easier. Thanks to Elliot Wallace for putting everything into perspective. Many others are left unthanked because we have to go to press as deadlines are looming.

The crew of the TV series 'E numbers – an edible adventure' have been long-suffering (nobody should have to watch me cook with my own body fat) and unbelievably hard-working. They were: Bruce Badenhorst, Isobel Briggs, Doug Bryson, Nicky Clark, Tim Cockroft, Will Daws, Will Edwards, Ian Holt, Steve Hopkins, Kari Lia, Rebecca Magill, Gabriella Martin, Dan Mellanby, Will Pugh, Mario Sierra, Sean Smith, Emily Rudge, Jo Walker, Toni Williamson, and everyone else who joined the team.